Sydney Opera House

Sydney Opera House
How it was built and why it is so

Written and illustrated
by
Michael Pomeroy Smith

To Diana and the children,
large and small

© Text and Illustrations MICHAEL POMEROY SMITH 1984

First published 1984 by William Collins Pty Ltd, Sydney
Published 1986 Michael Pomeroy Smith, Sydney
Reprinted 1991, 1993, 1997 Michael Pomeroy Smith, Sydney
Typeset by Post Typesetters, Brisbane
Printed in Hong Kong
Designed by Anna Warren

National Library of Australia
Cataloguing-in-Publication data

Smith, Michael Pomeroy,
The Sydney Opera House.

ISBN 0 00 217310 7

1. Sydney Opera House (Sydney, N.S.W.)
Pictorial works.   I. Title.

725′.822′099441

Introduction

The Sydney Opera House was a wonderful concept. To construct it took the designers and builders beyond the known limits of technology—it was a great effort by many people leading to breathtaking solutions of complex problems and an utterly delightful building.

How to tell the story of the Opera House is a problem in itself! It would take many volumes to cover all the different aspects thoroughly. This book sets out to tell the story in a short and simple way, so it has been pruned to the essential points. It starts by explaining why the theatres and halls came to be located where they are, then it describes how the main parts of the structure were put together, step by step, in words and drawings.

Contents

A Tale of Two Theatres

The Three Dimensional Cross

All theatres are built to help the performers create an atmosphere, or an illusion, for the audience. The shape of a traditional theatre is a cross in three dimensions — one arm for the audience, the stage in the middle, with the remaining five arms of the cross supporting it.

Sydney Opera House

Jørn Utzon, Architect, designed the theatres for the Opera House to fit the shape and setting of the rocky peninsula on which they were built. The two theatres were placed side by side so that they both had extensive harbour views. Utzon knew that the harbour, with its shipping and lights, would make going to the theatre a marvellous and exhilarating experience, so he designed the foyers to take full advantage of these sights.

Because the building would be seen from all sides, even from above, it was to be a piece of sculpture. The outside was as important as the inside.

Things to notice about the THREE DIMENSIONAL CROSS of the Opera House:

1 The audience enters from behind the stage and walks around to the foyers overlooking the harbour.
2 The wings and backstage areas are small because of the way the foyers wrap around the theatre.
3 The stage is made up of large platform lifts which provide the vertical movement for changing scenery. The sets come up from the workshops below stage.
4 The flytower fits under the largest roof shell and doesn't break the skyline.

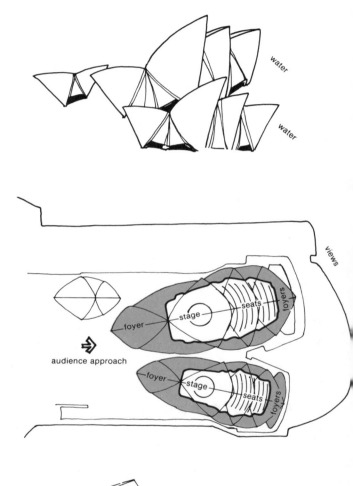

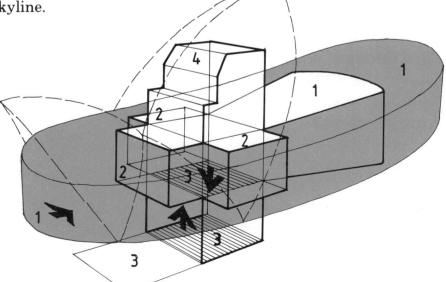

A Traditional Theatre

A traditional theatre has an atmosphere created inside the building. What is outside is not so important.

The site is usually in a main street, between other buildings, and its front (or facade) is the only part of the building noticed.

Things to notice about the THREE DIMENSIONAL CROSS of the traditional theatre design:

1 The audience enters from a foyer, at the back of the auditorium, and walks through to their seats. The foyer wraps around the theatre, but being in front of the stage it does not restrict the size or shape of the wings or backstage areas.

2 The deep wings are used for trundling scenery on and off stage and for assembling crowds of performers, out of view of the audience.

3 The deep backstage is useful for creating illusions of depth. This area is also used for access from one side of the stage to the other, as well as for all deliveries via the loading dock.

4 The stage area is repeated at either side and at the back of the stage. The movement for changing scenery is horizontal.

5 There are below stage lifts for special effects.

6 The high flytower is usually above the roof line, not confined within it.

Everything is designed for the convenience of the performers and stage technicians, with dressing rooms, toilets, rehearsal rooms all close to the backstage area.

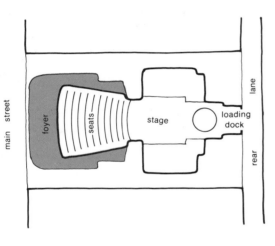

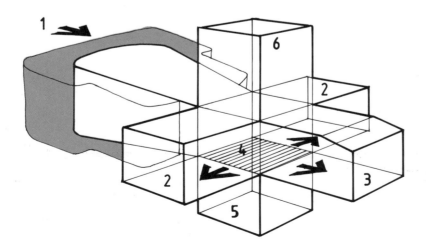

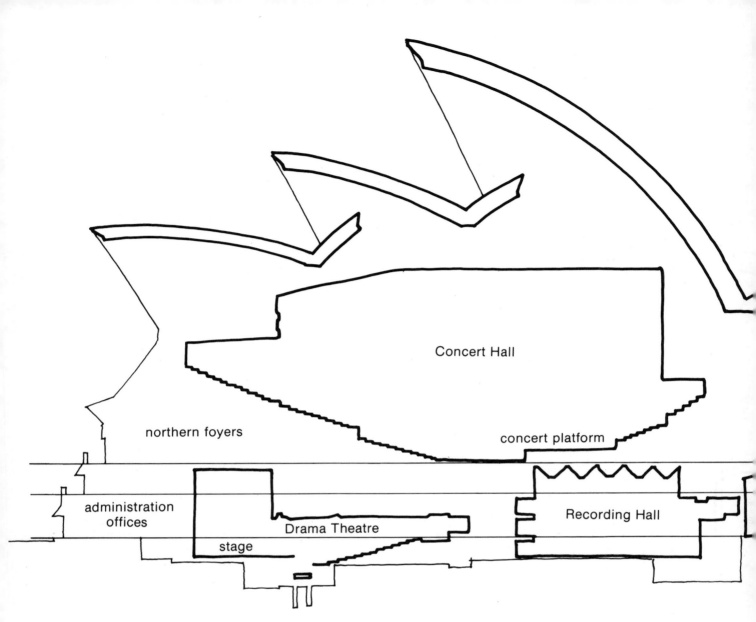

Concert Hall

northern foyers

concert platform

administration offices

Drama Theatre

Recording Hall

stage

SECTION THROUGH CONCERT HALL WING

SECTION THROUGH OPERA THEATRE WING

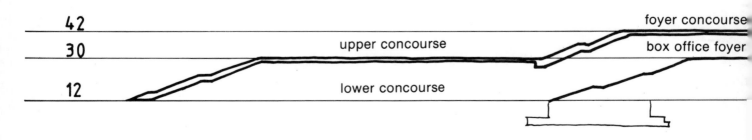

42

30

12

foyer concourse

upper concourse

box office foyer

lower concourse

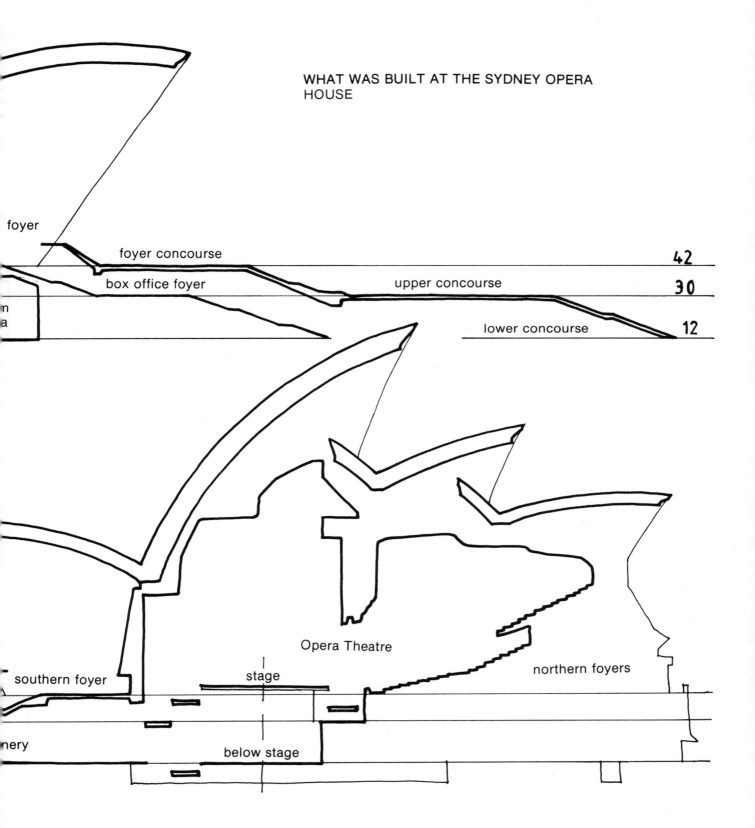

WHAT WAS BUILT AT THE SYDNEY OPERA
HOUSE

foyer

foyer concourse   42

box office foyer   upper concourse   30

                                    lower concourse   12

Opera Theatre

southern foyer   stage   northern foyers

nery   below stage

Background Notes To What Was Built

Some of the problems of the design and construction of the Opera House, that affected the final solutions, were:

Who Wanted What: When Utzon won the 1957 competition there was a list of spaces to be included in the building but no precise detail. It was nine years before the Australian Broadcasting Commission and the Elizabethan Theatre Trust fought out their differences and the exact needs were made clear to the designers.

Starting Too Soon: There was great pressure from the politicians to make the builders start work before things had been sorted out properly.

Unique Construction: The Opera House was something special. No one had designed or built anything like it before and a great deal of original thinking, testing and experimentation was needed before the real building work could start.

Dual-Hall Concept: Providing a reverberation time to suit both orchestral concerts and operatic voices. Providing enough seats to pay for the performances, yet ensuring good views and acoustics to all. Combining the needs of a stage for full scale opera with a platform for an orchestral concert with choirs and organ.

The Time Problem: 1957 to 1973 — sixteen years — people and their wants evolve and change over the years and new techniques are discovered that affect the original concepts.

Sound Is Energy: Sound travels in waves and takes time to fade away. This time will be shortened if the sound is absorbed (the energy is soaked up by crowds of people or soft materials). The time will be lengthened if the sound is reflected (the energy is bounced off hard surfaces).

Too much absorption means that sound will not travel far enough therefore people at the back of the hall will not hear properly.

Too much reflection means that sound will echo hence people will hear the same sound more than once.

The quality of musical sound is measured by the length of time it takes to fade away, called reverberation time (r.t. for short). Two seconds is considered pleasing for orchestral instruments (r.t. 2.0). One point four seconds is considered pleasing for voice (r.t. 1.4), measured in the middle frequencies of the sound waves.

The volume of a hall must be great enough to enable sound to travel the optimum distance for quality before it fades.

Sounds of music and voices need to be distributed evenly throughout the hall so that people sitting at the back can hear properly. Even distribution and avoidance of distortion can be arranged by placing walls and ceilings of specially selected materials and shapes in the right places. Acoustic experts, architects and engineers, make scale models of halls to test their theories before building a theatre. This was done at the Opera House.

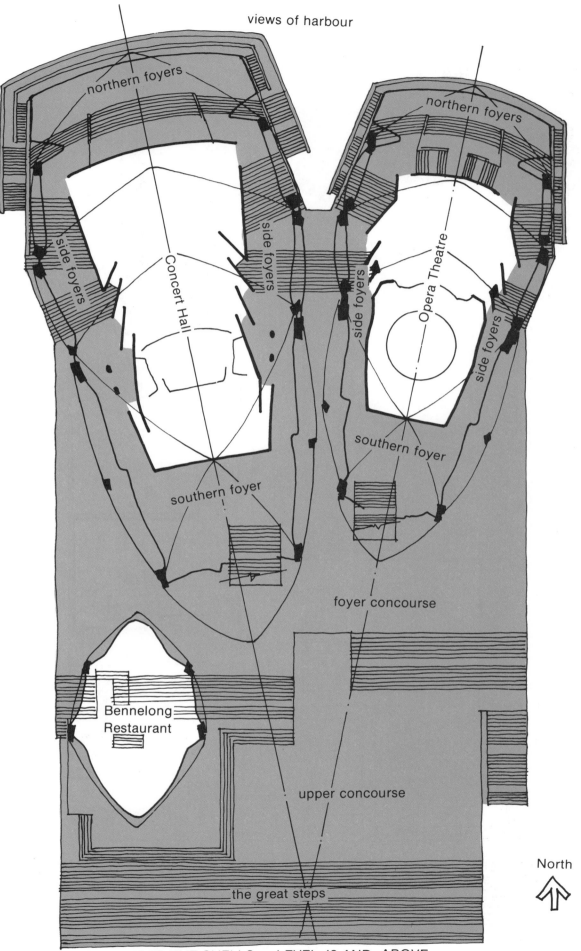

views of harbour

northern foyers

northern foyers

side foyers

side foyers

Concert Hall

Opera Theatre

side foyers

side foyers

southern foyer

southern foyer

foyer concourse

Bennelong
Restaurant

upper concourse

the great steps

North

11

PLAN — UNDER THE SHELLS — LEVEL 42 AND ABOVE

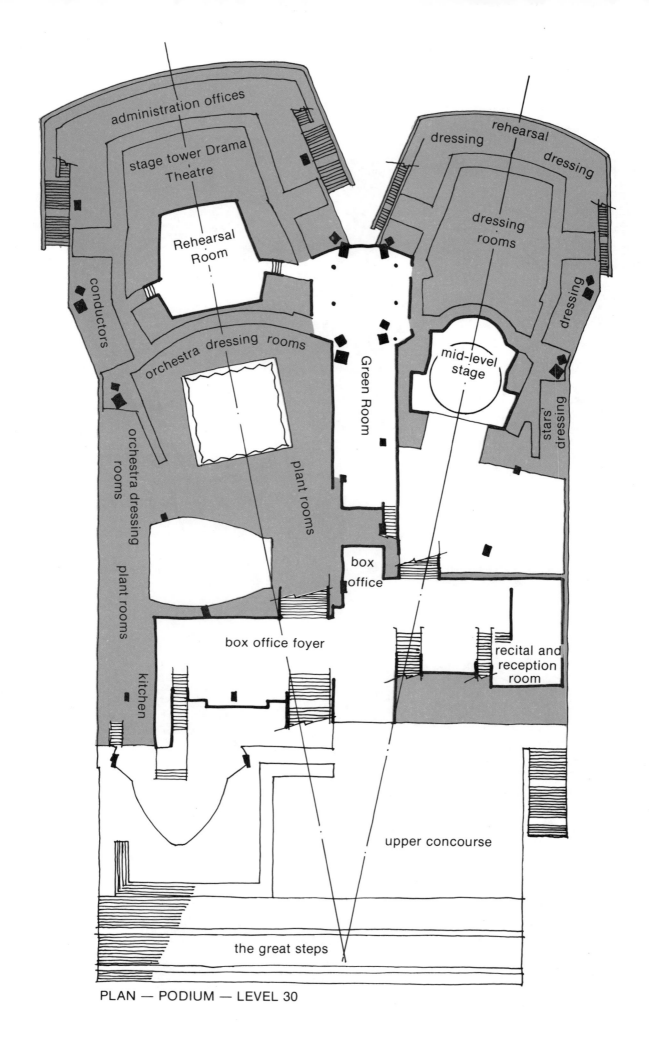

administration offices

stage tower Drama Theatre

Rehearsal Room

conductors

orchestra dressing rooms

orchestra dressing rooms

plant rooms

plant rooms

kitchen

dressing

rehearsal

dressing

dressing rooms

dressing

stars' dressing

mid-level stage

Green Room

box office

box office foyer

recital and reception room

upper concourse

the great steps

PLAN — PODIUM — LEVEL 30

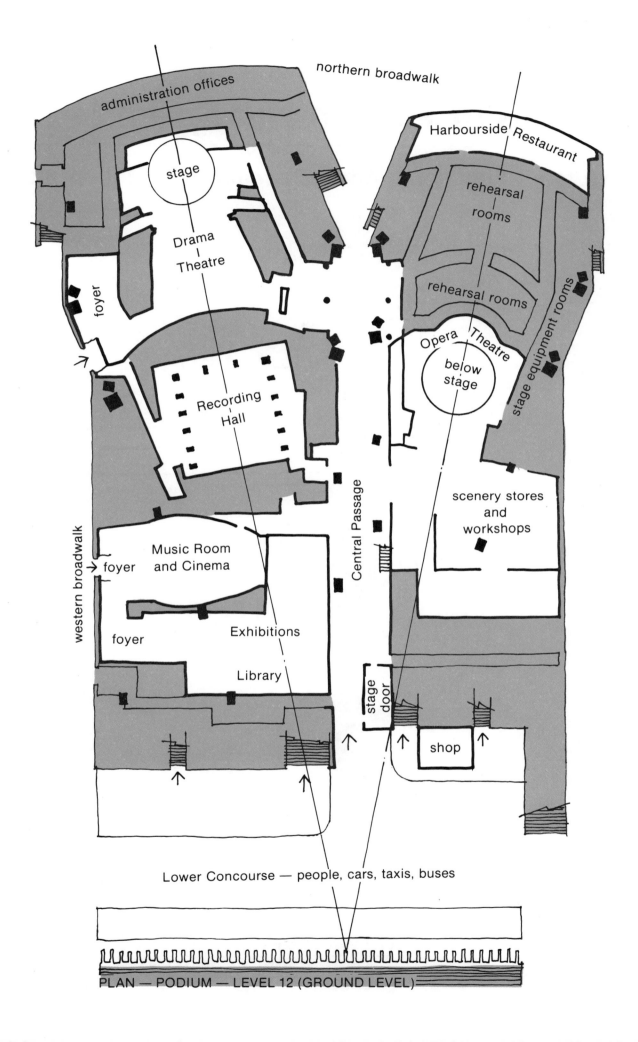

administration offices

northern broadwalk

stage

Drama
Theatre

foyer

Harbourside Restaurant

rehearsal
rooms

rehearsal rooms

stage equipment rooms

Opera Theatre

below
stage

Recording
Hall

Central Passage

western broadwalk

foyer

Music Room
and Cinema

scenery stores
and
workshops

foyer

Exhibitions

Library

stage
door

shop

Lower Concourse — people, cars, taxis, buses

PLAN — PODIUM — LEVEL 12 (GROUND LEVEL)

Why It Is So
Problems of Volume and Space

1 How to Fit Functional Areas Beneath Beautiful Forms

The Opera Theatre Solution

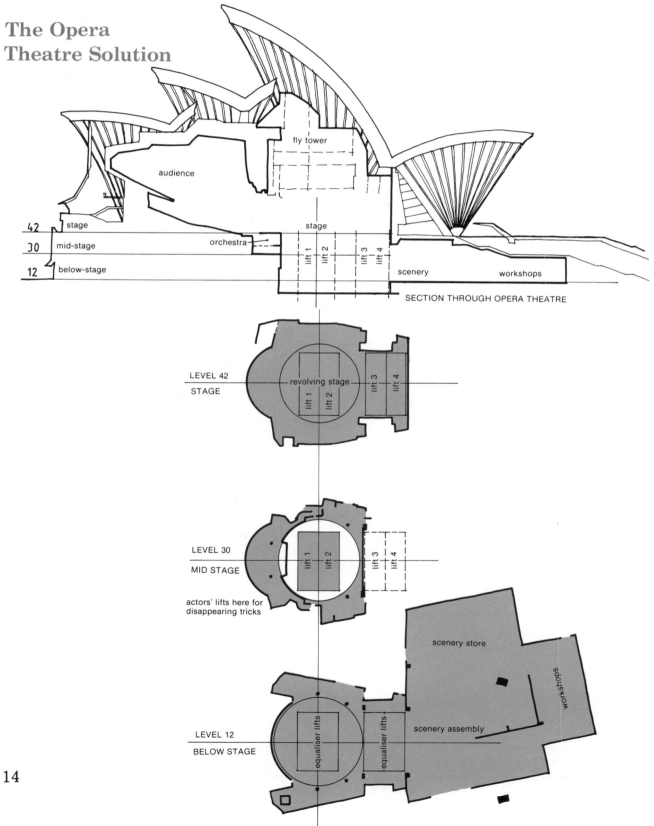

SECTION THROUGH OPERA THEATRE

LEVEL 42
STAGE

LEVEL 30
MID STAGE

actors' lifts here for
disappearing tricks

LEVEL 12
BELOW STAGE

14

Vertical Movement Was the Answer and Here Is How It Works

The scenery is built below stage, moved up on platform lifts to stage level and lowered when not required. The lifts are stacked like a removalists' van. All the scenery is placed on low mobile platforms, called trucks, which can be rolled across the floor. The setting of the scenery is done at stage level.

How the Scenery Is Changed

There are two floors, one above the other. The stage is on top and its floor has four big lifts in it, as well as a revolving stage. The floor underneath, called below stage level, also has four lifts or equalisers, which provide a floor when the stage platforms are raised.

The Theory (Pictures 1-3)

The sets are built on trucks (low platforms), which have electric motors to drive them, and are moved forward to the stage lifts. The sets are then lifted up to stage level and rolled forward on to the revolving stage. For quick scene changing the revolve turns and the used set is lowered to the assembly area.

What Usually Happens

For many performances the stage settings are small and the sophisticated equipment is not needed. In these instances the sets are built on small trucks and only the rear lifts are used.

However, when spectacular settings are needed, the sophisticated equipment cannot be utilised to advantage because of a built-in problem. In 1966, when the orchestra pit was enlarged, it took a section out of the revolving stage area. Now, when a full orchestra is required, the revolve cannot be used.

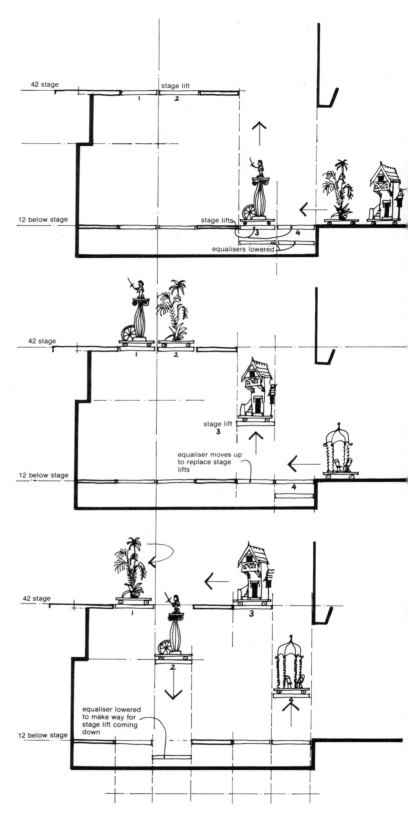

Problems of Volume and Space

2 Oboes Versus Sopranoes — The Concert Hall Solution

1957 — What The Architect Was Asked To Do

Utzon was asked to design a major hall suitable for both symphony concerts and opera performances. In this *dual purpose* hall he was to fit *enough* seats for concerts (where seeing the orchestra is not as important as hearing it) and *well-placed* seats for opera (where seeing and hearing are both very important). When used for opera the theatre would need the complete stage mechanics on the vertical movement principle. The auditorium was to be designed so that speech would be heard as clearly as music. This was a formidable task. Architect, acoustic expert and stage designer spent years working on a suitable design.

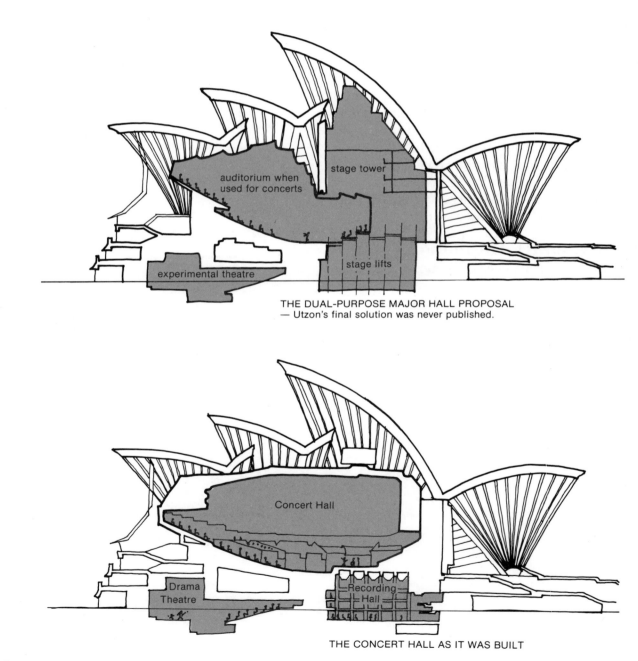

THE DUAL-PURPOSE MAJOR HALL PROPOSAL
— Utzon's final solution was never published.

THE CONCERT HALL AS IT WAS BUILT

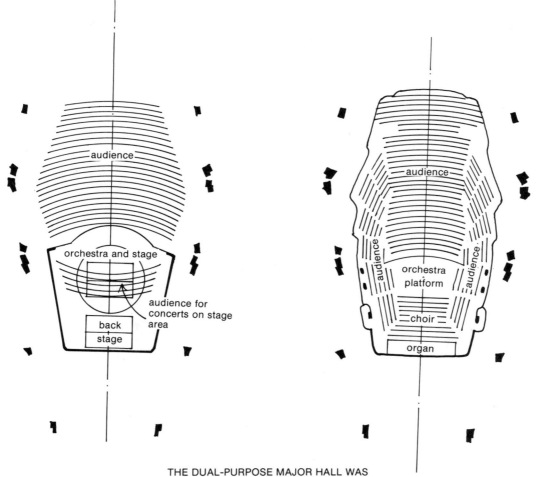

THE DUAL-PURPOSE MAJOR HALL WAS
CHANGED INTO THE CONCERT HALL

1966 — Why the Major Hall Changed Its Use

Three things happened in a short time. Utzon resigned. The Australian Broadcasting Commission, who were to use the hall for concerts, laid down strict terms about seating and reverberation times for their music — the oboes were winning! Next, Hall Todd Littlemore, the new architects, and the State Government, decided that the Dual Hall would be used for concerts only, and that the opera could move into the minor hall. This meant that work that was well advanced had to be scrapped, including the vast stage machinery.

1967 — How the Concert Hall Changed Its Shape

The stage, now a platform for the orchestra, was moved nearer the centre, and more seating added around it. The choir stalls were placed behind the orchestra, with the grand organ framing the end wall. The acoustics were now being designed for music and, as more volume was needed, the ceiling was pushed upwards and the walls backwards under the shells. More seats were gained by cantilevering galleries out over the foyers. However, there were no aisles, but there was plenty of leg room between each row for the audience to reach their seats.

Problems of Volume and Space

3 Beneath the Main Hall Stage — the Recording Hall

RECITAL IN THE RECORDING HALL

As the Concert Hall no longer needed a full theatrical stage the huge space below, where all the stage machinery would have been, was now empty. The experts worked out how to turn this space into a rehearsal and recording studio because its shape, a cube, was ideal for music acoustics. There was also an opening in the stage to be filled, and this was a problem. The big cranes were now *outside* the shell roofs and could no longer reach *inside*. The steel beams had to be manhandled into position and a thick concrete slab poured on top.

18

The Galleries

On all sides there were galleries that had been built for storage of the scenery. Three were turned into places where the audience could watch and listen. Because of their shape they helped to absorb sound. The fourth side was filled with sound control booths and equipment.

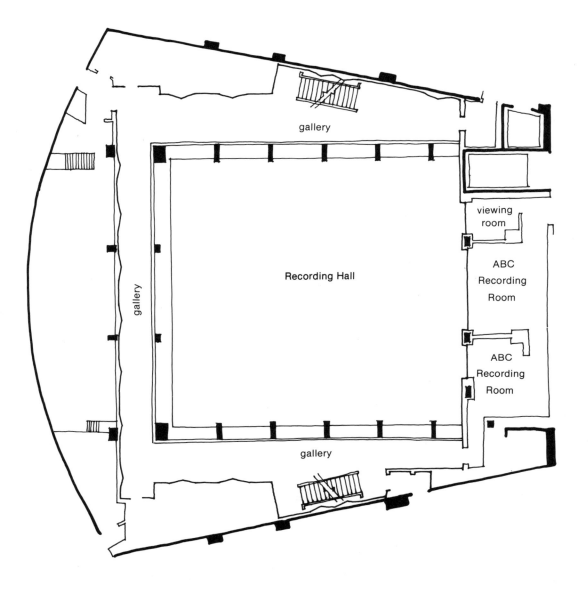

Noise From Outside must not be allowed to upset the recordings. All six sides of the cube had to be isolated from the rest of the Opera House. A box within a box. To break up sound waves it is very effective to pass them through mass, void, then mass again, so a double skin of concrete was poured. Each skin was separated from the other by neoprene pads forming an air space. All doors were sound proofed.

Noise From Inside must be controlled so that it is heard without distortion. The ideal length of time for music is between 2.0 and 2.1 seconds — if too long, it echoes — if too short, it is lost too soon. The walls and ceiling were made to absorb or reflect sound as needed, so the ceiling is a special shape and all surfaces that absorb the sound are lined with slot-perforated plywood panelling, with mineral wool backing.

Problems of Volume and Space

4 A Jigsaw Puzzle Down in the Podium — the Drama Theatre

This theatre was designed by Utzon as a four hundred seat experimental theatre but in the big turn around, after 1966, it became the Drama Theatre with five hundred and forty-four seats. It fits into the podium like a piece of a jigsaw with its stage beneath the Concert Hall. The pit for the stage lift, and the orchestra pit, are below sea level and the water is kept out by the mass of concrete, rock and steel casing.

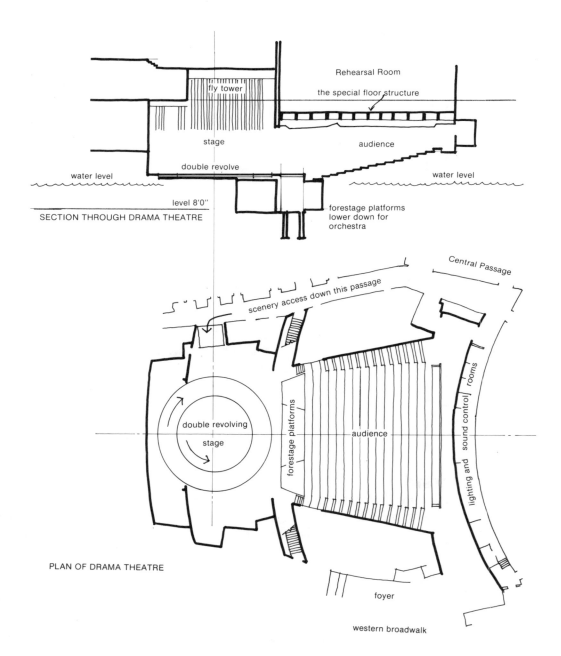

Scenery and the Stage

Scenery, delivered to the Central Passage, is taken down a corridor and squeezed through a doorway, then up in a lift. Extra large pieces are carried in through the auditorium. The stage has a double revolving floor and a forestage platform that can be lowered to create an orchestra pit for thirty-five musicians. The proscenium is long and narrow, nicknamed 'the letter box'.

A Concrete Waffle

This structure, between the Drama Theatre and the Rehearsal Room above, is the roof of one and the floor of the other. The span across the hexagon-shaped theatre was too great for a flat slab of concrete, so the structural engineers, Ove Arup and Partners, designed a square-ribbed concrete frame, with reinforced concrete beams crossing each other at right angles. It looks like a giant waffle iron from underneath.

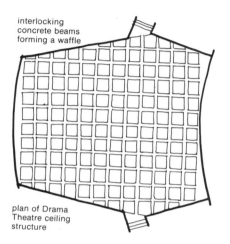

interlocking concrete beams forming a waffle

plan of Drama Theatre ceiling structure

An Unusual Air-Cooled Ceiling

People seated in an enclosed space create a lot of heat and they need fresh air. An air conditioning system usually blows cool air in at ceiling level but if this had happened in the Drama Theatre the audience would have felt uncomfortable as the ceiling is low. The mechanical engineers, Steensen Varming, designed a ceiling that absorbed heat rising in the theatre by passing cool air through hollow aluminium panels. There were slots between the panels for outside conditioned air to provide sufficient ventilation. Here is how it works:

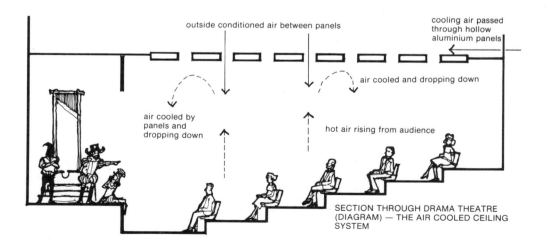

outside conditioned air between panels

cooling air passed through hollow aluminium panels

air cooled and dropping down

air cooled by panels and dropping down

hot air rising from audience

SECTION THROUGH DRAMA THEATRE (DIAGRAM) — THE AIR COOLED CEILING SYSTEM

21

Problems of Volume and Space

5 The Auditorium Cocoons

There are structures like huge cocoons nestling under the shells of the Opera Theatre and Concert Hall. If you look upwards from the side foyers you can see the concrete sails soaring over the tops of the auditoriums. These cocoons enclose light and sound. The inside of an auditorium must be a special shape so that sound waves are distributed evenly. Music and voices must be guided to the audience but noise must not be allowed in from outside, nor must noise travel to a nearby theatre. Many experts helped to find the best shapes for the insides of the cocoons and several models were made.

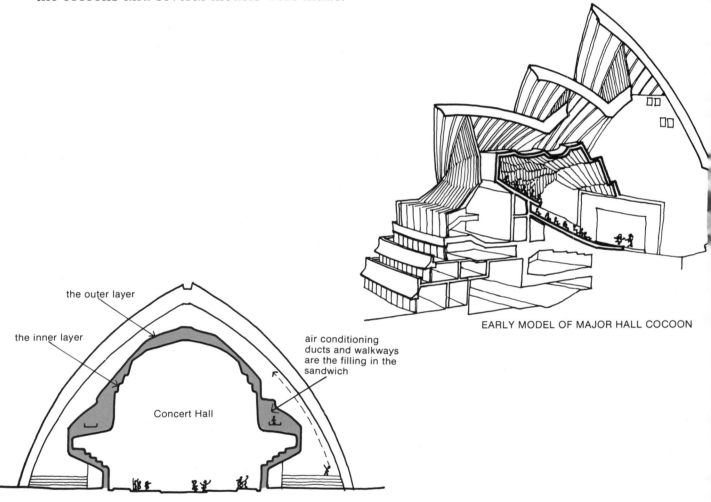

EARLY MODEL OF MAJOR HALL COCOON

CROSS SECTION THROUGH CONCERT HALL

the outer layer

the inner layer

air conditioning ducts and walkways are the filling in the sandwich

Concert Hall

The Walls of the Cocoons — a Special Sandwich

The Outer Layer — a thin layer of concrete sprayed over steel mesh and asbestos sheeting, then fibre glass insulation held on by chicken wire. The whole skin was supported on a steel framework which was free-standing of the concrete shells, except for connections at a few strong points.

The Inner Layer — what is seen from the auditorium is white birch plywood. This is fixed in panels to a timber framework. The back of each panel is padded with plasterboard to deaden the sound of the plywood vibrating from the sound waves, but not to kill the sound entirely — this is why there are gaps at all the edges.

Plywood Panels Located by Computer

Each plywood panel was a particular shape. A computer worked out the exact dimensions and location, then the panels were hoisted up and attached in just the right place, independent of each other.

The filling in the sandwich consists of air space with walkways, ladders, ducts, electric cables, light fittings, etc. The distance between the two layers of the sandwich varies a great deal because of the shapes.

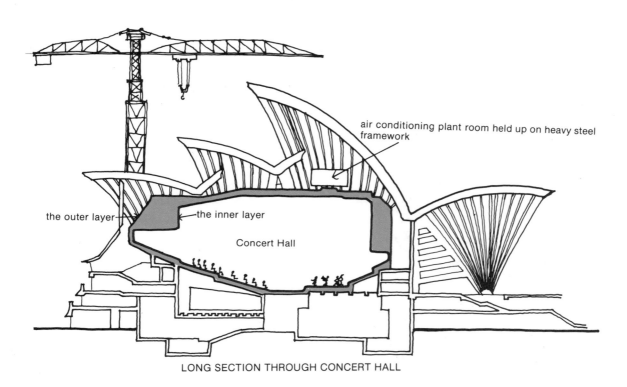

LONG SECTION THROUGH CONCERT HALL

How to Hold Up the Air Conditioning Machinery Over the Concert Hall? Work on Sundays When It's Quiet!

After 1966, when it was decided to change the use of the main halls, and to air condition them both at the same time, more air conditioning plant was needed and a three-storey room had to be built over the Concert Hall. The heavy steel could not be lifted in by the tower cranes because the roof shells were completed. The steel was squeezed in through the hole in the stage floor by a Hornibrook team working on Sundays when it was quiet. The winch drivers could not *see* the riggers but could *hear* them as they called out or whistled — during a noisy week day they couldn't have done it.

Problems of Volume and Space

6 Movement of People and Things

Three groups of people come to the Opera House — the performers (and their supporting staff); the audience and visitors and the Opera House working staff, (who also divide into three groups — administration and technical, catering and cleaning, front of house). On a busy occasion there can be six thousand people there, so the building was planned in zones to suit their movements.

Zones for Staff, Technicians, Performers and Goods

The Stage Door — the main check point and nerve centre of the security system. The stage door is actually a room that functions as waiting area, information desk, security check, with warning lights and control panels for electrical, mechanical and fire-fighting installations throughout the building.

The Green Room — a long hall between the Opera Theatre and Concert Hall on the dressing room level. It is the main artery and crossroads of the theatrical working side of the Opera House where people congregate before, during and after performances. The cafeteria, bar and lounges are used by all staff and there are telephones, intercoms and closed-circuit television screens for communications.

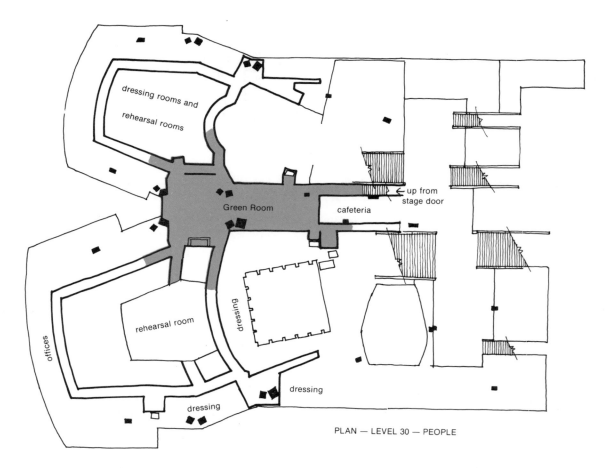

PLAN — LEVEL 30 — PEOPLE

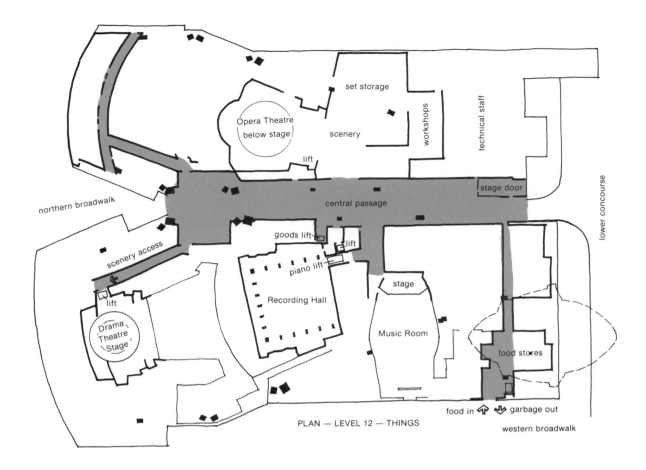

set storage

Opera Theatre
below stage

scenery

workshops

technical staff

lift

stage door

northern broadwalk

central passage

lower concourse

goods lift

lift

scenery access

piano lift

lift

Recording Hall

stage

Drama
Theatre
Stage

Music Room

food stores

PLAN — LEVEL 12 — THINGS

food in ⇗ ⇘ garbage out

western broadwalk

The Central Passage — at Level 12 (ground) is a road right down the middle of the podium. Goods on trucks are delivered via the Stage Door check point and on a typical day you might see pieces of scenery, theatrical props, orchestral instruments in their travelling cases, forklift trucks, utility vans, ABC outside broadcast TV vans, trolleys of food heading for the restaurants, building materials and all manner of things.

LOW CLEARANCE
11 FT 6 IN

CAUTION

STAFF
TECHNICIAN STAGE DOOR

EXIT

THE CENTRAL PASSAGE —
handicapped and elderly going to the lifts

Zones for Audiences and Visitors

Box Office Foyer and Foyers Surrounding Main Halls

The main route to the Opera Theatre or Concert Hall is through the Box Office Foyer. It contains the ticket office, cloakrooms, a cafe, telephones and information desk. It stretches nearly the width of the podium, located between the car concourse and the southern foyers and connected to both by impressive flights of steps. These steps lead up under a canopy of concrete to burst out under the magnificent vaults.

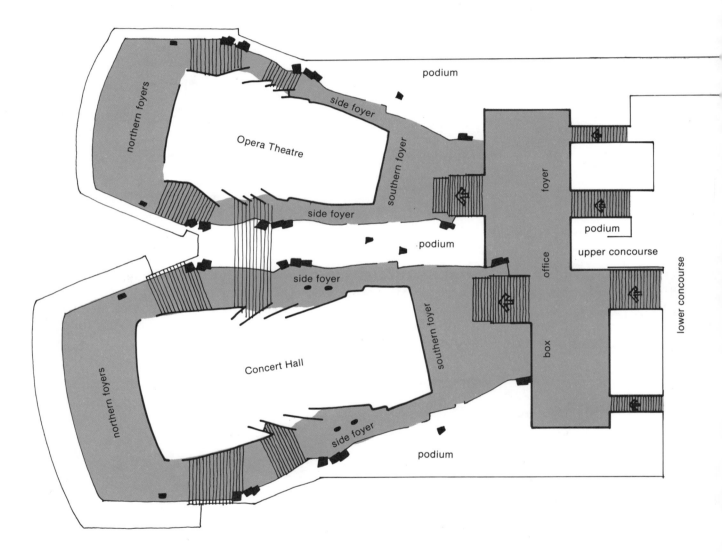

The foyers surround the two main halls in an identical manner. The southern and side foyers are linked by the glass walls with the podium outside, and steps lead up and over to the northern foyers and the panorama of the harbour. There are doors into the auditoriums along each side, and doors through the glass walls directly to the podium and open air, in case of an emergency. Drinks and light refreshments are served in the foyers, and small concerts and receptions are held on the terraces of the northern foyers.

The Broadwalks and Surrounds

The broadwalks, concourse steps and podium deck outside the glass walls, are open to the public all the time. The Drama Theatre, Music Room (Cinema), Recording Hall, Exhibition Area and Library are all entered off the western broadwalk. The Harbourside Restaurant opens on to the northern broadwalk. The Bennelong Restaurant, under its own set of shells, is on the podium and is entered from the Box Office foyer. Open air entertainment takes place at various points of the public areas.

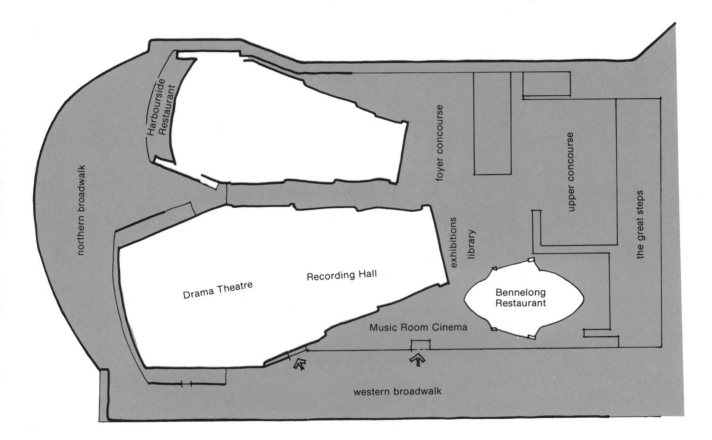

How the Staircase Problem is Solved

All audience routes up to the two main halls involve climbing stairs. The elderly, infirm or handicapped who cannot manage them are taken through the Stage Door into the Central Passage, where there are lifts. These lifts go up to the side foyers of the Opera Theatre and the Concert Hall. There are other lifts off the Central Passage for goods and scenery, including large lifts for grand pianos, which serves the Recording Hall and the Concert Hall.

How It Was Done

1 The Podium

A Solid Base

If the shell roofs were taken away, together with everything under them (Concert Hall, Opera Theatre, surrounding foyers, restaurant) then the major part of the Opera House would still be there! This is the huge monolithic concrete structure called the Podium. It contains hundreds of rooms and nearly all the technical equipment needed to keep the whole complex working.

Seen From the Water

The podium is clad with pink granite slabs. The stone was crushed and the pieces selected to give a uniform colour, then made into panels. Utzon had wanted the podium to 'float' over the water by keeping the cladding above high water level. However, the design was changed so that the cladding goes right down and now has a high tide mark of marine growth on it.

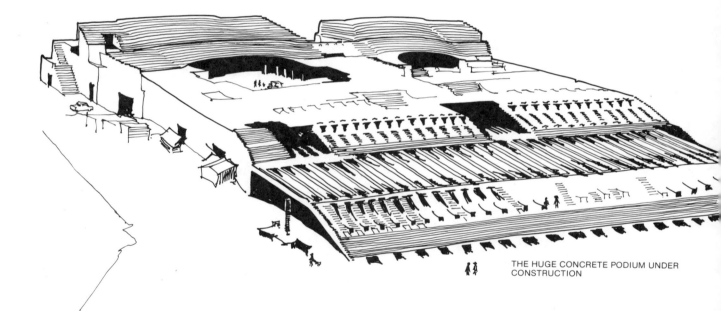

THE HUGE CONCRETE PODIUM UNDER
CONSTRUCTION

For Safety and Convenience

Utzon needed to be able to move thousands of people *out* of the theatres rapidly if there was an emergency. He also wanted an impressive base upon which to unfurl the magnificent sail roofs. He combined these two requirements by arranging the podium platform to surround each theatre so that the audience could move out quickly on all sides to the open air. This design eliminated a maze of fire escape stairs and, at the same time, gave people a wonderful view of the harbour. Utzon's solution was brilliant and simple.

Seen From Inside

The concrete is finished 'off-form' just as it was poured into the timber supports. The formwork was in three grades:

1 very smooth and neatly joined (public view)
2 lesser quality (and cheaper) for less important places
3 bare basic for out-of-sight places

Plywood Covers

Most of the pipes, wires and ducts are covered by removable plywood cover pieces fixed to walls and ceilings.

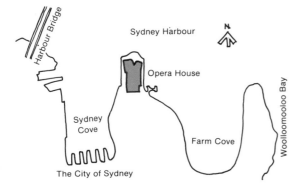

The Foundations

The Opera House is built on a peninsula of rock that juts out into Sydney Harbour.

The site was once a landing place for ships. It was built up around the edges with stone sea walls and the water sloshed in through the joints between the stones. Behind the walls was rubble filling lying on the rock. The rock had seams and faults in the upper layers, so the foundations were carried right down through it into the solid rock below.

Around the edges about seven hundred holes were bored and then filled with concrete. The bottoms of these holes were well below water level, so steel tubes were driven down to keep the water out whilst the concrete was being poured. In the centre of the site, above water level, the concrete footings were poured directly on to the rock.

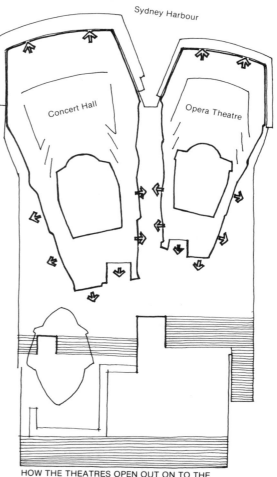

HOW THE THEATRES OPEN OUT ON TO THE PODIUM

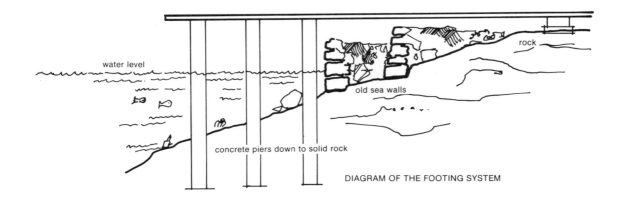

DIAGRAM OF THE FOOTING SYSTEM

29

The Concourse Beams

Right across the land approach to the building is a very wide, very impressive flight of steps. These steps are divided into two flights with a landing in between. Steps and landing cover the car concourse and are held up by specially shaped concrete beams of huge span. Originally, Utzon showed columns supporting this structure, but later he asked Arup to design beams that would span right across and down the slope without columns. He wanted the beams to express, by their shape, the stresses they would bear. Arup produced a bold and striking design.

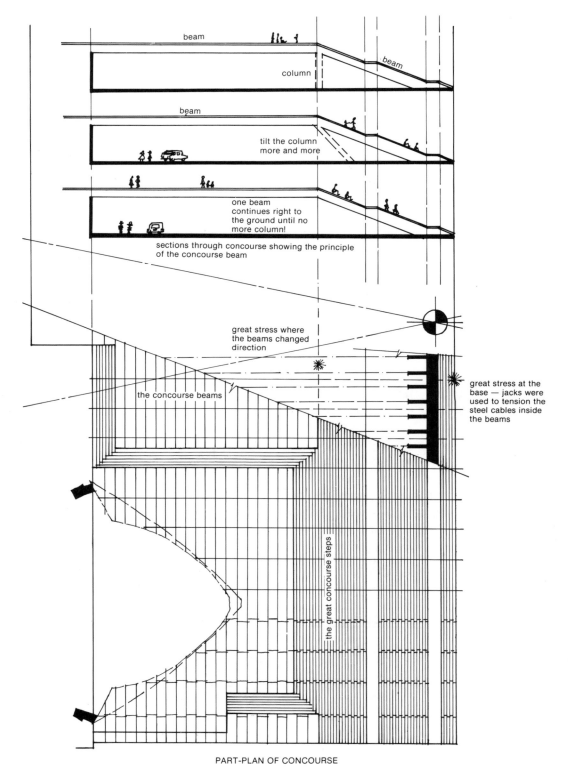

beam

column

beam

beam

tilt the column
more and more

one beam
continues right to
the ground until no
more column!

sections through concourse showing the principle
of the concourse beam

great stress where
the beams changed
direction

the concourse beams

great stress at the
base — jacks were
used to tension the
steel cables inside
the beams

the great concourse steps

PART-PLAN OF CONCOURSE

Post Tensioning

To counteract the great stresses, steel cables were put inside the beams and pulled tight (tensioned) by means of jacks. The beams were now able to join together without sagging under the weight of people, or stone covering, that would go on top of them.

They were loaded with weights to see just how tight the cables would have to be. Because there was no solid rock at the foot of the struts concrete footings were built and the jacks stretching the cables were strained against them. When the steel cable was tight enough steel wedges were driven in to jam it in place.

When is a Column Not a Column?

Something special had to be done with the beams if they were to span the distance. The columns were tilted out until they became struts, or extensions of the beams themselves. These shaped beams were under great stress at two places, one where the horizontal piece butted into the sloping piece, the other where the foot of the strut pressed down on the foundations.

Unusual Gutters

An interesting side effect, from the shape of the beams, is that they are gutters for the rain water collected on the podium. Utzon wanted the podium paving to be flat and designed joints between the slabs to let the water through into the gutter shapes formed by the beams underneath.

How the Beams Changed Shape

Sometimes the main stress is in the top of a beam, sometimes in the bottom. Arup designed it so that when more concrete was needed at the top, it looked like a letter T, when more concrete was needed at the bottom, it looked like a letter U. They arranged for the beam to change shape in a smooth flowing way, all done with straight lines in cross section, so no material was wasted.

HOW THE BEAMS CHANGED SHAPE — CROSS SECTIONS FROM T TO U

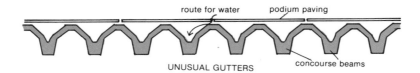

route for water   podium paving

UNUSUAL GUTTERS   concourse beams

31

How It Was Done

2 The Shells

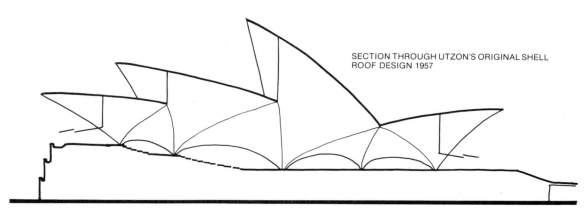

SECTION THROUGH UTZON'S ORIGINAL SHELL ROOF DESIGN 1957

Nature's Own Shell Structures

An egg shell is remarkably strong — try squeezing one between your hands (but not over a carpet!). It transmits the stresses all around, although in cross section the wall of the shell (membrane) is very thin.

KRESGE AUDITORIUM M.I.T. Eero Saarinen

an egg shell is very thin and very strong

Egg Shells of Concrete

By the 1950s, architects and engineers had succeeded in developing an imitation of egg shells with thin concrete. These early shell roof designs were not able to be solved absolutely by the mathematics of the time, but they proved themselves by standing up. Several had been built around the world, including designs by Eero Saarinen, one of the judges of the Opera House competition. Utzon was confident that his winning design could be built, even though it was 'free-form' in shape and not defined by regular geometry (which would have made the mathematics easier for the engineers).

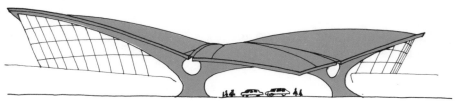

T.W.A. TERMINAL, IDLEWILD AIRPORT, N.Y. Eero Saarinen

Explorations and Evolutions

Arup's engineers tried to define precisely:

1 the shapes of Utzon's concept

2 the form of the stage towers that the shells would have to cover

3 the loads the shells would have to carry, such as tile coverings and ceiling structures

SKETCH OF UTZON'S DESIGN

STRUCTURAL MODEL OF SHELL ROOF UNDER STRESS TEST

A model of the single skin shell roofs was made in Denmark and tested in England. It was discovered that a single skin simply wouldn't do the job. A double skin shell was tried, with the skins separated by webs like an egg carton, but the mathematics could not be solved to the engineers' satisfaction, nor the finished appearance to Utzon's approval.

Arups, with Utzon by their side, worked very hard for six years — 1957 to 1963 — to solve the problem. They used a computer extensively and tried, in several schemes, to make each shell support the others. They were very concerned that if one fell it would topple all the others, like dominoes.

After many trials and investigations Utzon and Arup concentrated on precast concrete, factory made units, joined together to make fan-like ribs. Then came the breakthrough — Utzon evolved the spherical geometry solution.

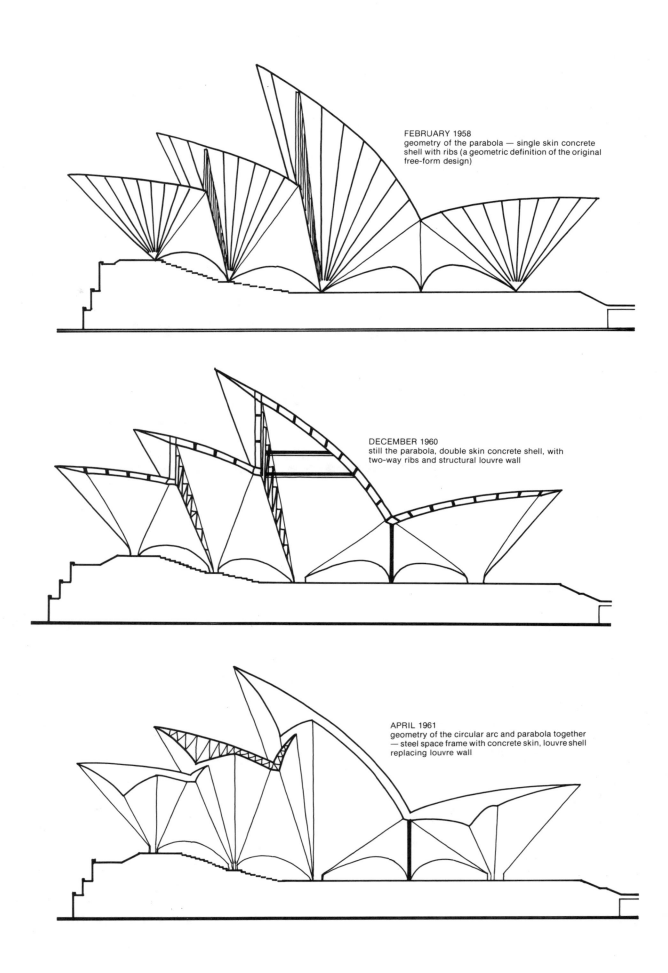

FEBRUARY 1958
geometry of the parabola — single skin concrete
shell with ribs (a geometric definition of the original
free-form design)

DECEMBER 1960
still the parabola, double skin concrete shell, with
two-way ribs and structural louvre wall

APRIL 1961
geometry of the circular arc and parabola together
— steel space frame with concrete skin, louvre shell
replacing louvre wall

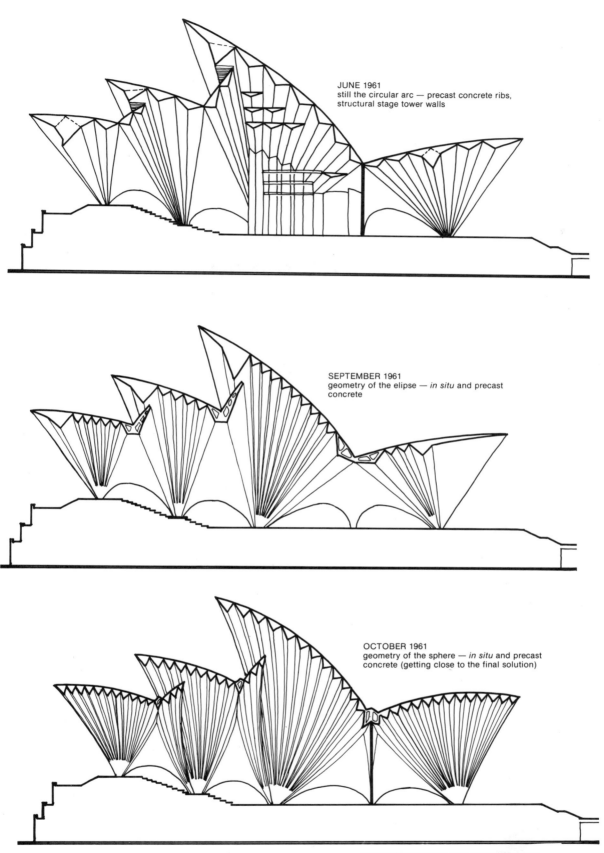

JUNE 1961
still the circular arc — precast concrete ribs,
structural stage tower walls

SEPTEMBER 1961
geometry of the elipse — *in situ* and precast
concrete

OCTOBER 1961
geometry of the sphere — *in situ* and precast
concrete (getting close to the final solution)

THE EVOLUTION OF THE GEOMETRY AND
STRUCTURE OF THE ROOF DESIGN — from shell
concrete to concrete ribbed arches 1957 to 1963

Utzon's Spherical Geometry and the Final Solution

Utzon realised that the *regular form of a sphere* could be so sliced and dug into as to give all the pieces needed for *ribs that repeated the same curve.*

This meant that all the rib sections could be made from only a few moulds. This looked like simple, economic prefabrication, and it was!

Utzon had a wooden sphere made in a shipyard in Denmark and excitedly he cut out the pieces. Arup worked with him and confirmed his ideas and together they solved the problem.

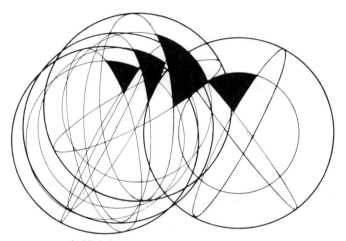

the black shapes are the four main shells coming out
of a series of overlapping spheres

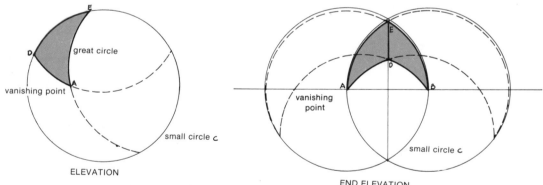

ELEVATION

great circle radius 246' 0"
small circle radius 211'0"

END ELEVATION

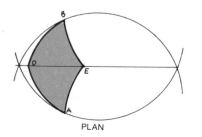

PLAN

UTZON'S SPHERICAL GEOMETRY
detail of how the ribs in the shells evolved from the
spheres

How the System Worked

Each shell is made up of many ribs, tied together with steel cables.

Each rib is in two halves, arch like, joining together at the ridge.

Each rib is made up of many segments glued to each other and tied together with steel cables.

Each segment is made from a common set of geometrically shaped moulds. The concrete moulds were on the site and the segments were lifted into position by crane.

The shells are actually made up with a series of ribbed arches all joined together — they are not like the thin membrane of an egg shell (or concrete shell) but the name stuck. The roofs of the Opera House are still referred to as 'the shells'.

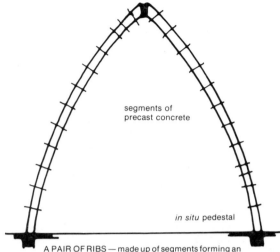

segments of
precast concrete

in situ pedestal

A PAIR OF RIBS — made up of segments forming an arch when joined together

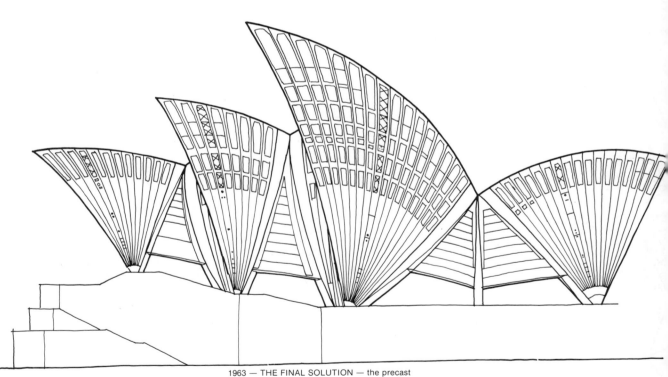

1963 — THE FINAL SOLUTION — the precast concrete ribbed arches join together to make up a series of shell roofs

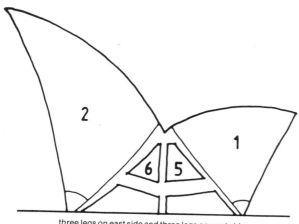

three legs on east side and three legs on west side —
a solid six legged structure

How the Vaults Joined Together

The design that evolved was self-supporting — no dominoes! Here's how the shells stand on their own feet:

Main shells 1 and 2 are back to back and connected to each other by pairs of side shells (side shells 5 and 6 west and 5 and 6 east are really one shell divided by a massive concrete leg that goes down into the podium). This group of shells form one solid unit held up on six legs.

Main shell 3 is not connected to either shell 2 or shell 4, although it stands between them. They could be taken away and shell 3 would still stand up! This is because it, too, is back to back with louvre shell 9 and joined to it by side shells 7 east and 7 west, making another solid, self-supporting unit, held up on four legs. Main shell 4 is held up the same way, with louvre shell 10 and side shells 8 east and 8 west.

plan of main shells
1 and 2 and side
shells 5 and 6

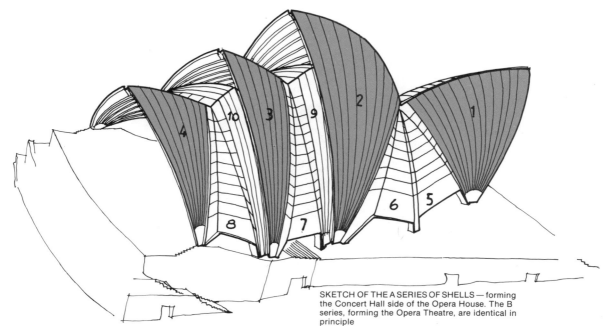

SKETCH OF THE A SERIES OF SHELLS — forming the Concert Hall side of the Opera House. The B series, forming the Opera Theatre, are identical in principle

39

How It Was Done

3 Up Go the Sails

Problems Down in the Podium

The podium had been started in a rush because the politicians wanted things moving. The engineers had had to guess the sizes for the footings to support the roof shells. In those early days they thought the roofs would be made from thin concrete shells — in fact the roofs were to be made with heavy ribbed arches. The foundations that had been built were not strong enough.

An Explosive Solution

To overcome the problem the builders had to thicken the concrete pillars. They found the best way to join new concrete on to the old was to drill holes into the piers, fill the holes with explosives and blow the piers up! This they did, bursting the concrete aside to reveal the steel reinforcement inside — just like peeling a banana. The new concrete was then keyed on to the exposed steel. Deep down in the podium the thunderous bangs of the explosions echoed round and round and things were assembled ready for building the great sails over the top.

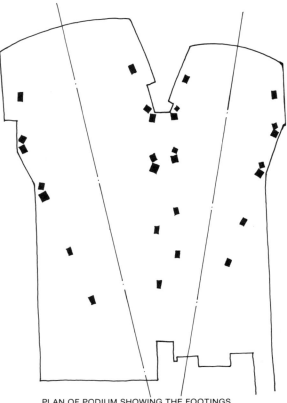

PLAN OF PODIUM SHOWING THE FOOTINGS FOR THE SHELL ROOFS

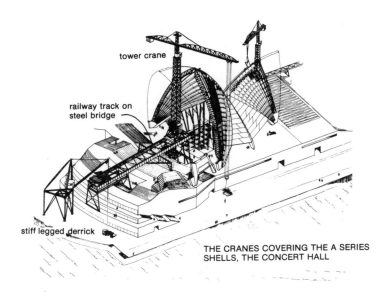

tower crane

railway track on steel bridge

stiff legged derrick

THE CRANES COVERING THE A SERIES SHELLS, THE CONCERT HALL

The Cranes

Three giant tower cranes were brought from France. They were shipped over in pieces, thirty truck loads for each crane, and built on the site. They were modified Babcock Weitz G280B cranes.

Two to the north, one to the south, the cranes were mounted on special steel bridges like huge railway tracks, so that they could move along and cover the whole site.

Smaller cranes, called stiff-legged derricks, were positioned near the foot of each tower crane to lift things on to a waiting platform.

How much they could lift at a particular distance from the masthead governed the weight, and therefore the size of the concrete segments being made below.

PLAN OF CRANE COVERAGE OF THE SITE

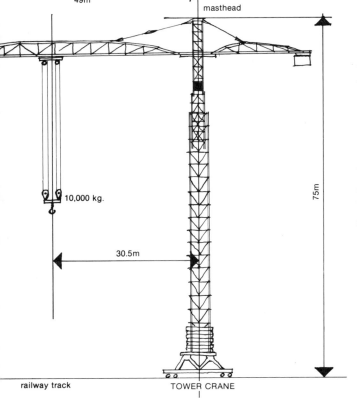

It was established that the cranes could lift ten thousand kilogrammes at a distance of thirty point five metres from the masthead. This distance covered the site adequately, so the concrete rib segments were made to weigh a maximum of ten thousand kilogrammes.

The length of the segment was governed by this weight and all segments were made the same length, four point six metres, except the top ones on each side of the arch — these were shorter.

41

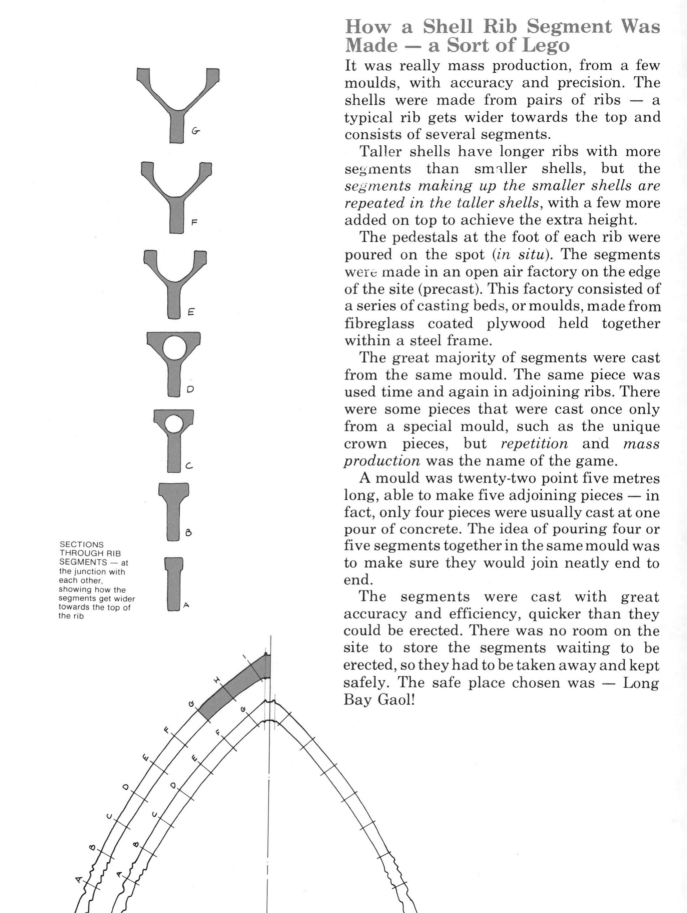

SECTIONS THROUGH RIB SEGMENTS — at the junction with each other, showing how the segments get wider towards the top of the rib

THE TALLER RIBS — made from the same segments as the shorter ribs plus some more segments added to the top of the rib

How a Shell Rib Segment Was Made — a Sort of Lego

It was really mass production, from a few moulds, with accuracy and precision. The shells were made from pairs of ribs — a typical rib gets wider towards the top and consists of several segments.

Taller shells have longer ribs with more segments than smaller shells, but the *segments making up the smaller shells are repeated in the taller shells*, with a few more added on top to achieve the extra height.

The pedestals at the foot of each rib were poured on the spot (*in situ*). The segments were made in an open air factory on the edge of the site (precast). This factory consisted of a series of casting beds, or moulds, made from fibreglass coated plywood held together within a steel frame.

The great majority of segments were cast from the same mould. The same piece was used time and again in adjoining ribs. There were some pieces that were cast once only from a special mould, such as the unique crown pieces, but *repetition* and *mass production* was the name of the game.

A mould was twenty-two point five metres long, able to make five adjoining pieces — in fact, only four pieces were usually cast at one pour of concrete. The idea of pouring four or five segments together in the same mould was to make sure they would join neatly end to end.

The segments were cast with great accuracy and efficiency, quicker than they could be erected. There was no room on the site to store the segments waiting to be erected, so they had to be taken away and kept safely. The safe place chosen was — Long Bay Gaol!

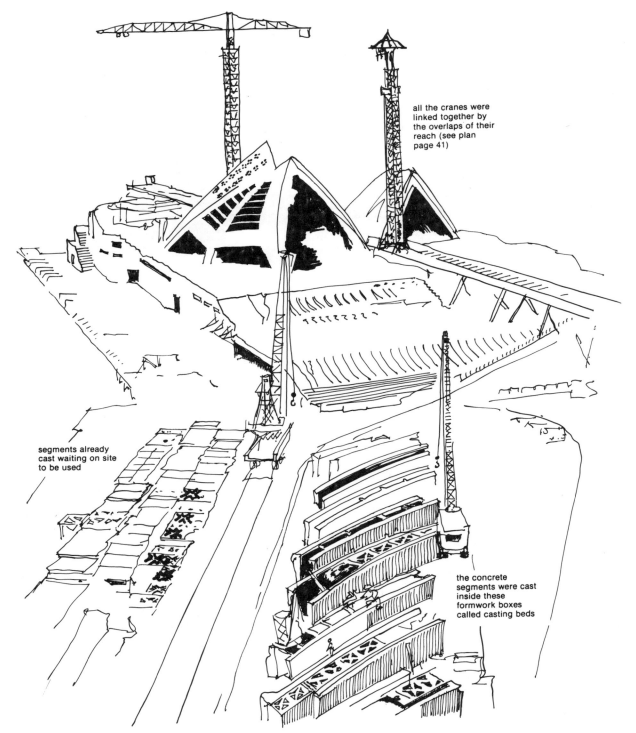

all the cranes were
linked together by
the overlaps of their
reach (see plan
page 41)

segments already
cast waiting on site
to be used

the concrete
segments were cast
inside these
formwork boxes
called casting beds

THE CASTING BEDS — an open air factory on the
edge of the site

43

The Order in which the Parts Were Put Together

Step One

The strong base framework for the roof structure was formed by the four triangles of side shells 5 and 6 east, and 5 and 6 west. These were built first.

The sides, of each side shell triangle, are made up with segmented arches, similar to the main shell ribs, but different in that these arches are warped. They are hollow concrete boxes in cross section and are built up in segments.

Because of their warped shape there is some intricate geometry where the side shells join to the regular spherical curves of main shells 1 and 2.

Step Two

The pedestals were built next — the concrete was poured *in situ*. These pedestals were the springing point for all the main shell ribs.

Step Three

Next came the pairs of ribs, made up from their segments to form arches. The first pair of ribs was erected on the steelwork supporting the side shells.

Step Four

The second, and subsequent, pair of ribs was supported on the Hornibrook steel erection arch and the previous ribs. So the pairs of ribs were built up until the shells 1 and 2 were completed.

The same process was repeated for all the other shells.

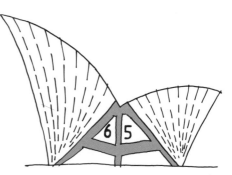

side shells 5 and 6 east and west formed a strong triangular base

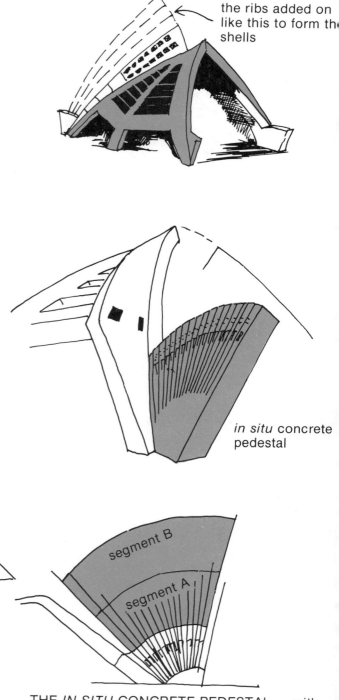

the ribs added on like this to form the shells

in situ concrete pedestal

segment B

segment A

THE *IN SITU* CONCRETE PEDESTAL — with segments radiating up from it

44

Placing a Segment

When a rib segment was ready for placing on top of an already laid segment, the new block was taken by lorry to one of the two stiff-legged derricks. The derrick lifted the block to the foot of one of the tower cranes which picked up the block in a special slinging cradle. This cradle was able to tilt the block in any direction. The block was then lowered to just above its exact spot, between the rib already built and the steel erecting arch.

The precise positioning of each segment was worked out by a complicated survey using a computer for calculations — this survey stated exactly where each segment should be in the air above the podium.

When a segment was just about in place the builders spread epoxy glue (looking like condensed milk) on the bottom of the segment and on the top of the one waiting to receive it. This was to make sure that all surfaces touched and that the stress would transfer evenly and smoothly right down the rib. It was then lowered to rest on top of the block below.

Finally, the new block was stressed. Roof segments have cables running through them from pedestal to crown piece. There were nine stressing cables used for erection and they only went from the first segment to the top segment. When the rib was erected, additional stressing cables (varying in number from ten to twenty-one), were stressed in three locations right from the pedestal to the top segment.

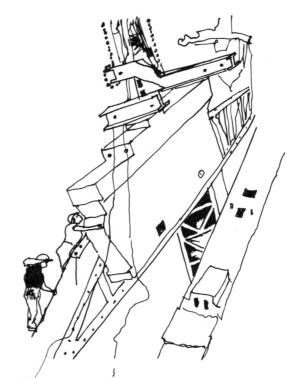

PLACING SEGMENT A — the first segment on top of a pedestal

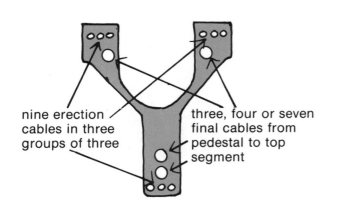

nine erection cables in three groups of three

three, four or seven final cables from pedestal to top segment

CROSS SECTION OF A SEGMENT — showing the two groups of stressing cables inside the ribbed arch

PLACING THE RIDGE SEGMENT

45

The Hornibrook Steel Erection Arch in Action

Utzon, Arup and Hornibrook — architect, engineer and builder, worked together to solve the problems of how to erect the shells.

Hornibrook invented a special arch, made of steel, that could easily be altered in shape to suit each particular pair of ribs to be built. There were four of these arches on the job. Each steel arch was able to become a replica of a pair of concrete ribs. The steel framework was telescopic. It could be pulled out to suit a tall pair of ribs, or pushed in to suit a shorter pair. The arches could be moved horizontally along the podium by hydraulic rams and inclined to any angle — thus the steel arches could be made to duplicate exactly the dimensions and position of any pair of concrete ribs.

Because each pair of ribs was self-supporting and tied back to the pair behind, each new segment could be safely supported in the gap between the rib just built and the steel erection arch, until that whole rib was itself competed.

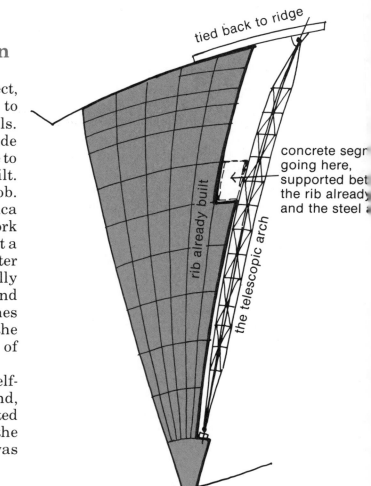

tied back to ridge

rib already built

the telescopic arch

concrete segr
going here,
supported bet
the rib already
and the steel

HOW THE ARCH SUPPORTED THE SEGMENTS

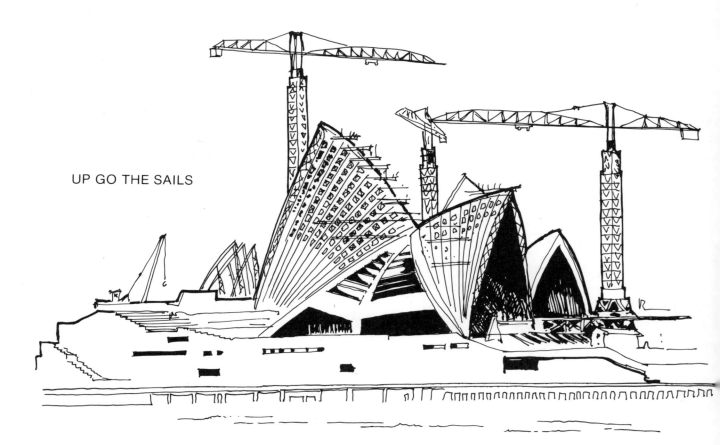

UP GO THE SAILS

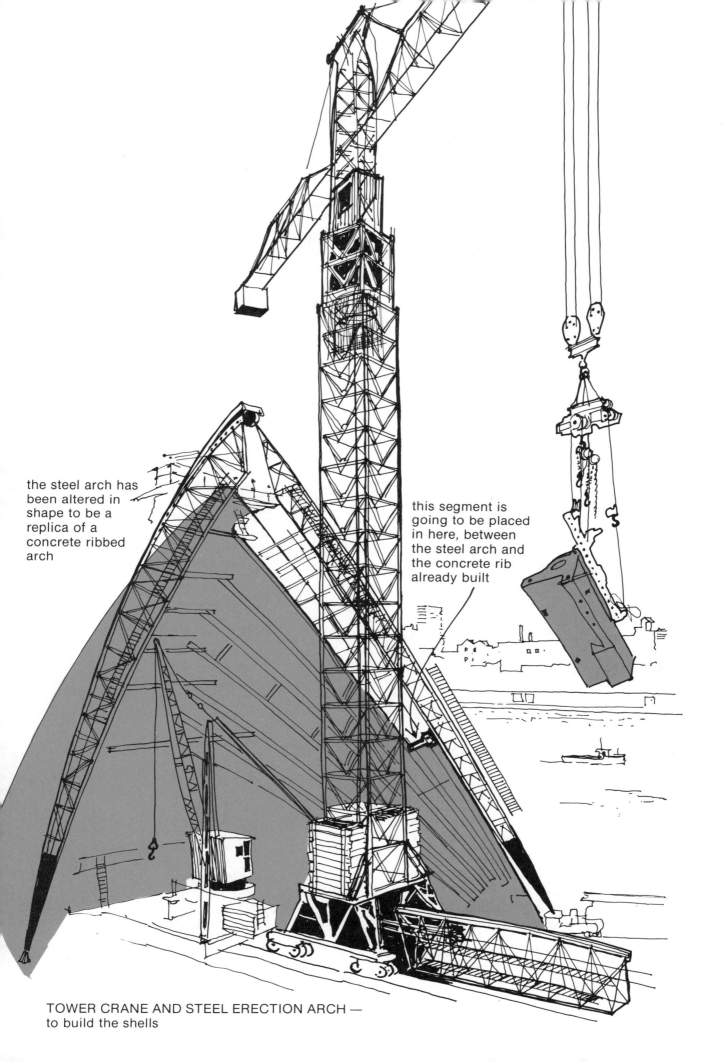

the steel arch has been altered in shape to be a replica of a concrete ribbed arch

this segment is going to be placed in here, between the steel arch and the concrete rib already built

TOWER CRANE AND STEEL ERECTION ARCH —
to build the shells

How It Was Done

4 Tile Lids to Cover the Roofs

The Idea — Utzon had great imagination and perception. He knew that the Opera House roof surfaces would be seen from above, all round, in all weathers and by day and night. He realised that glazed tiles would produce liveliness and interest on the roof surfaces under all the differing conditions of light.

The Technique — When Utzon had conceived the roofs as shell concrete structures his first thoughts had been to tile the surfaces in the traditional way, laying tile by tile, but this had caused him much concern as such huge areas of tile might not match each other or, tiles may even fall off! The possibility of forming regular, geometric, mass produced panels was one of the reasons that led him to redesign the roofs as ribbed arches in spherical geometry. The technique was to use tiles, laid in patterns, made into panels on the ground, so that there would be no mistakes. The panels would then be lifted up and fixed in position. The accuracy and control of manufacture and placing was just what he wanted and the panels would form a watertight lid.

What Sort of Tiles?

Utzon needed tiles that would be self-cleaning and good-looking. Careful searching led to Hoganas in Sweden. The tiles were a light colour, ceramic on top with rough texture underneath. Some of the tiles were matt finish, buff colour, while others were glazed finish and white.

The Subtle Pattern

The tiles were made into chevron shaped lids, white with buff borders. The shapes and sizes of the chevrons fitted over the segments in the roof ribs to reflect the anatomy of the structural form below.

This intricate pattern of the tiles provides a strong sense of geometry in the overall design.

There were more than one million tiles on four thousand two hundred and fifty-three lids, but only eight different types of tile. Because the lids followed the geometry of the ribs beneath they, too, gained from the economies of mass production. Some chevron lid patterns were repeated two hundred and seventy-six times, and three hundred and fifty-eight warped side shell lids were made from only four different moulds.

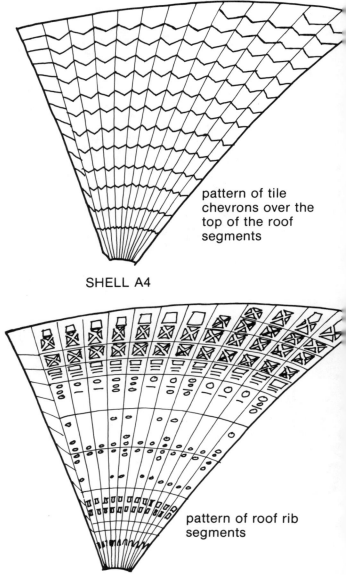

pattern of tile chevrons over the top of the roof segments

SHELL A4

pattern of roof rib segments

How a Tile Chevron Lid was Made

A factory was established on site to make the lids. First, the shape of a lid was formed from a concrete base curved to follow the spherical geometry of the roof. Next, a grid of aluminium strips was fixed to the concrete base to locate each tile accurately. Then steel plate sides were put around, shaped to have waterproofing grooves between the lids. The tiles could now be placed in position.

When the tiles were all in, laid face downwards, animal glue was poured between their joints to stop the cement showing on the face of the chevron. Galvanised steel mesh was carefully positioned over the backs of the tiles and a fine sand and cement mortar was then poured all over, making a ferro-concrete panel of the whole thing.

The panel was then steam cured. This was done at night to allow the daytime production to flow unhindered.

The condensation and melted animal glue ran out of the pre-cut grooves. When the lids were cooked they were given a steam clean on the outside and hung up to dry. For insulation each lid was given a backing of polyurethane foam sheets.

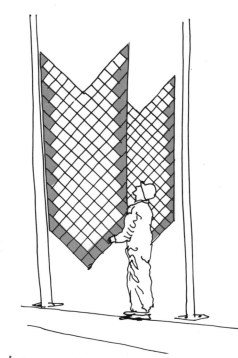

hanging chevron lids up to dry after steam curing and cleaning

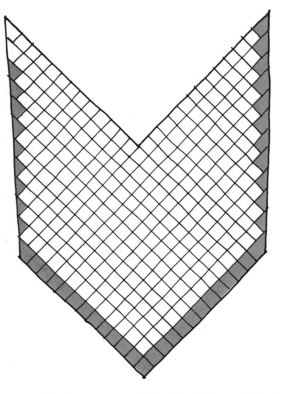

pattern of a chevron — white tiles in the middle, buff tiles around the edges

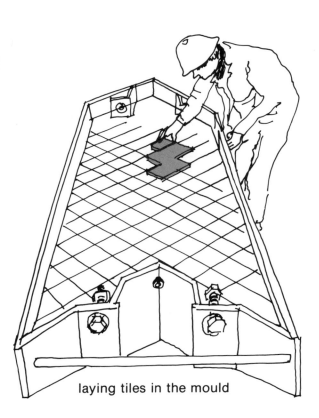

laying tiles in the mould

49

Fixing a Chevron

The principle was to be that each lid was fixed independently of another and that the fixing brackets would all be connected to the concrete roof beforehand. A chevron would be lifted up and slipped over the bracket waiting for it.

There were two basic types of brackets. The majority were a slip-over type (spigot and socket) which eliminated any tiling on the spot. The others were a bolt-up type which meant that the last tile had to be fixed on the spot to cover the nut and bolt.

The waiting bolts and spigots were on the roof and the erection began.

Something Goes Wrong!

The first few chevrons were placed in position — so far, so good — then it was discovered that the next batch wouldn't fit. The chevrons were very slightly oversize and, due to miniscule faults, there was a creeping error — the sockets were not matching the waiting spigots!

Computer to the Rescue

The spigots and bolts, already fixed to the roof, were not able to be used in their locations. A technique was devised to place each chevron in its new position without regard to others. An accurate survey on ten thousand fixing bolts was done using a computer and many bolts were repositioned. Adjustments were fed from computer to the field teams to set and change the brackets before they lifted the lids into position. The rigger had a bag of nuts and washers and knew which ones were needed on each lid — thus, by a marriage of sophisticated surveying, with a versatile design for fixing brackets, the problem was solved.

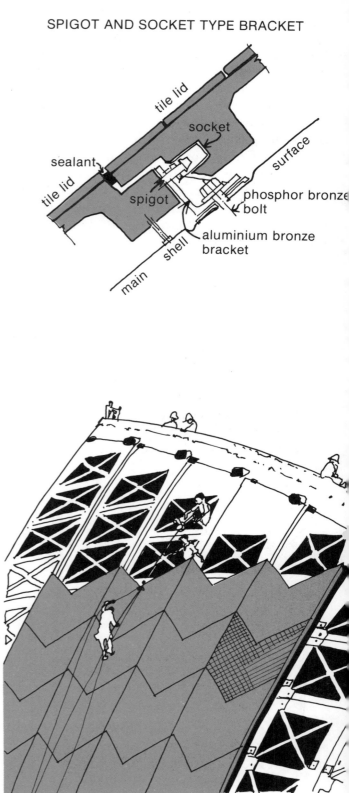

SPIGOT AND SOCKET TYPE BRACKET

tile lid

socket

sealant

surface

tile lid

spigot

phosphor bronze bolt

aluminium bronze bracket

shell

main

rigger, secured by ropes, fixing a tile chevron lid on to a main shell

50

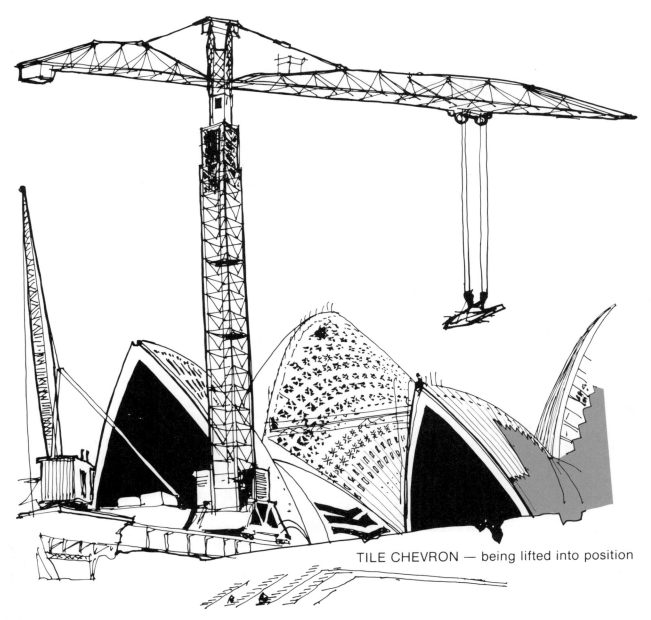

TILE CHEVRON — being lifted into position

Corrosion Worry

Once a tile chevron lid was fixed in position the brackets beneath it were impossible to reach, therefore the metal used for them had to be corrosion proof. It was also under stress. Finally, phosphor bronze was chosen for rods and bolts, and aluminium bronze for castings.

Waterproof Jointing

The joints between each tile were sealed with epoxy. The joints between each chevron were made by lead caulking and a none lastomeric sealer. Each lid was fixed independently of the others, to allow for expansion and contraction. All the joint sealers were flexible.

How It Was Done

5 The Glass Walls

Challenge and Excitement

When Utzon resigned in 1966, he left behind his aims and ideals for enclosing the shells with glass walls. We shall never see the glass walls as he visualised them, but the challenge was taken up by the architects, engineers and glass specialists and solved with the help of technology — and now they are an exciting reality.

The Architect's Requirements

Utzon wanted all the glass walls to be seen as one family of structures with each piece similar, and related, to the next piece. He visualised an uncluttered structure made up of thin, elegant pieces with as little obstruction as possible to vision, looking outwards or inwards. Also, the glass must keep out noise.

The glass walls were to hang from the concrete roof shells like curtains. They were to fan outwards at the northern foyers and the restaurant to cover more floor space than the shells covered overhead.

Therefore, the major problems to be solved by the engineers were that the glass walls should be strong, safe, watertight and soundproof.

The Choice of Glass

DANGER! The shape of the glass walls was such that over the northern foyers, and in the restaurant, the glass is as much roof as wall. Throughout the Opera House there were huge areas of glass suspended above the public — a real danger if the glass were to break and fall. Normal sheet or plate glass wouldn't be safe — laminated glass was chosen.

Why? When broken, sheets of laminated glass stick together (pieces don't fall down easily) and they will hold out the weather until replaced. Also, it could be cut easily to shape and it kept out more noise than other glass. Although these basic things were known at the time a research programme was set up to investigate thoroughly all aspects of laminated glass.

The Investigations — 1961-1971

Many different ways of holding up the glass were explored using different materials, including glass itself, aluminium and timber.

Laminated timber was the most favoured by Utzon and Arup, with bronze sheets hot bonded over plywood. However, although such mullions (as the vertical supports are called) would probably have held up, they were rather big at the bottom and the aims of slenderness and clear viewing were not being met.

Concrete was tried and rejected. In 1967 the team of engineers and architects from Arup and Hall Todd Littlemore worked out the principles of the final solution — a structural steel framework inside, supporting a corrosion-proof frame to hold the glass outside.

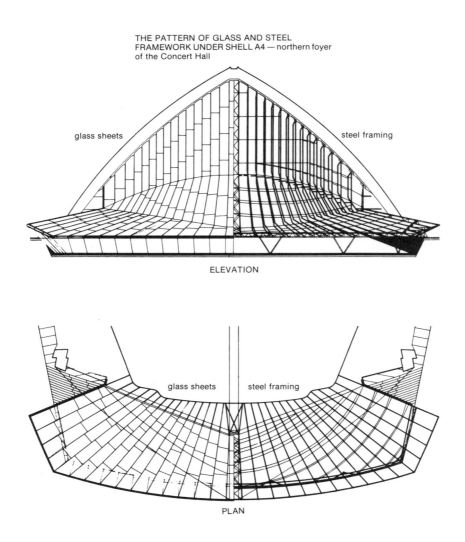

THE PATTERN OF GLASS AND STEEL
FRAMEWORK UNDER SHELL A4 — northern foyer
of the Concert Hall

glass sheets   steel framing

ELEVATION

glass sheets   steel framing

PLAN

How the Glass was Made

The glass had to be specially made for the job. The firm of Boussois Souchon Neuvesel in France made 'pot' glass and their techniques were chosen, partly because they could make just as much as was needed rather than having a huge production run. They poured coloured molten glass from a large pot on to a flat surface — this sheet of glass was six millimetres thick, coloured demi-topaze, and was bonded to clear float glass twelve millimetres thick, by means of a layer of clear plastic. The plastic was placed between the two sheets of glass and the sandwich was heated to bond all three pieces together — the glass, thus laminated, was then taken to Antwerp from where it was shipped to Sydney.

How the Glass is Held Up

A steel framework takes the weight. This framework has an outer framework fixed to it which holds the glass. The outer framework must not corrode and is made from manganese bronze. It was most important that the inner, supporting framework, would remain stiff at all times and would not bend under the load of the glass and the outer frame. Steel is a good material for this task if assembled the right way. Specially shaped mullions were built up from parallel tubes joined by a flat plate web — they, and all the other steel parts, were made with great accuracy in the factory of J.W. Broomhead (Constructions) Pty Ltd. All the complicated connections were worked out so that the whole framework would fit together perfectly when each piece was brought to the job. Although it was expensive to build the framework off-site, much time was saved on-site when it fitted perfectly. The steel was painted a colour to be in harmony with the granite paving of the podium.

Erection of the Steelwork

There was no room for creeping error! The whole frame had to fit. The surveyors set up control points in space using the techniques they had developed whilst building the shells. The steel was brought into its exact position as it was erected.

Starting with shell A4 (Concert Hall northern foyer) a concrete beam had been cast *in situ* around the rim of the shells. This beam, attached to fixing points on the shell that had been made for an earlier mullion design, was shaped to receive the mullions and to eliminate having to cut the glass to a sharp point. Each mullion was bolted to this beam, starting with the central pair and working outwards, left and right. The mullions were braced back to the building and to each other and connected to the ring truss. This truss had been set in space using computer guided survey controls. Progressively the whole framework was built up.

The Versatile Fixing Bracket

Although the steel frame was built very accurately, all the glass sheets were pre-cut and the slightest error would mean a misfit. Something had to be flexible, adjustable, giving tolerance to the system. Enter Hawker de Haviland Australia Pty Ltd, the aircraft people. They developed an aluminium bronze fixing bracket, that joined the high tensile brass glazing frame, to the steel support frame. It was able to adjust up, down, sideways and rotate too!

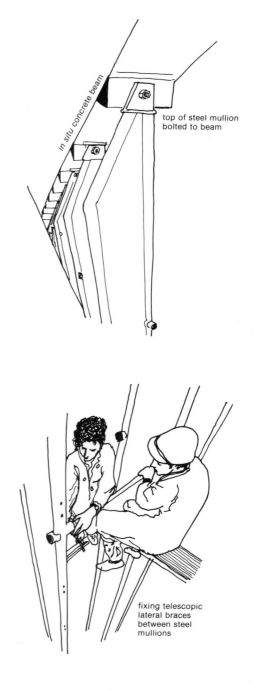

in situ concrete beam

top of steel mullion bolted to beam

fixing telescopic lateral braces between steel mullions

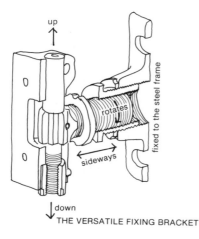

up

rotates

sideways

down

fixed to the steel frame

THE VERSATILE FIXING BRACKET

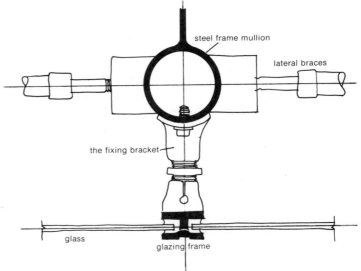

steel frame mullion

lateral braces

the fixing bracket

glass

glazing frame

54

Geometry of Glass Walls

Walls A4 and B4 northern foyers of Concert Hall and Opera Theatre:

The problem was that there was no mathematical relationship between the shape of the shells and the podium. The geometry was worked out so that the top part is defined by the shell ribs—which are based on spherical geometry, so a cylinder was chosen. The bottom part is defined by a cone, covering the podium. The middle part, another cone, joins the top and bottom together.

There was only one way to calculate all this—by computer. The engineers did it, using an I.C.L. 1900 series computer. Each set of glass walls had its own special problems. Walls A1 and B1 had to join on to the entrance canopies, and more computer work was needed.

The side walls could be defined by the side shell geometry and it was possible to cantilever the mullions down from the box beams to support a nosing, from which the glass could span down to the sill.

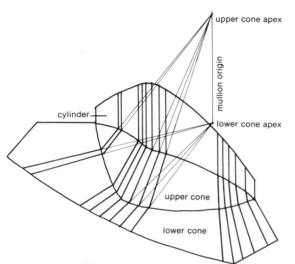

A4 and B4 GLASS WALL GEOMETRY — the shell roofs connected to the podium through cylinder, upper cone and lower cone

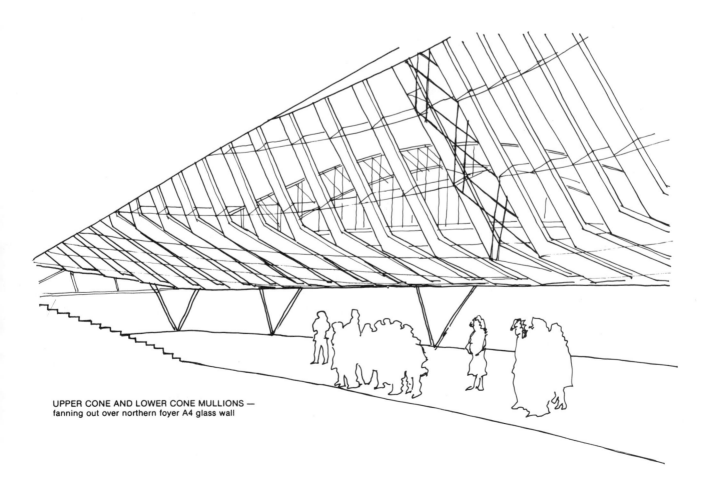

UPPER CONE AND LOWER CONE MULLIONS — fanning out over northern foyer A4 glass wall

Cutting the Glass

Seventeen kilometres of saw cut please!

The glass walls were like a three dimensional jigsaw puzzle. Each piece of glass had to be cut to shape from a rectangular blank and then fitted into its particular place. In order to achieve straight, perpendicular edges it was decided to saw the glass. The problem was how to cut so much glass to keep up with the production programme. The combination of circular diamond impregnated saw blades, from Diagrit Diamond Tools Ltd England, and ingenuity by Quick-Steel Engineering Pty Ltd, Australia, using two saws, did the job.

The sawing was done on a special rigid table, fitted with suction pads to hold the glass securely whilst being able to raise or lower sections at a time. The saws cut the glass on their first pass, then tilted and came back to angle the edges on their way back.

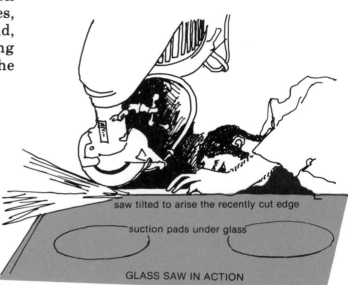

saw tilted to arise the recently cut edge

suction pads under glass

GLASS SAW IN ACTION

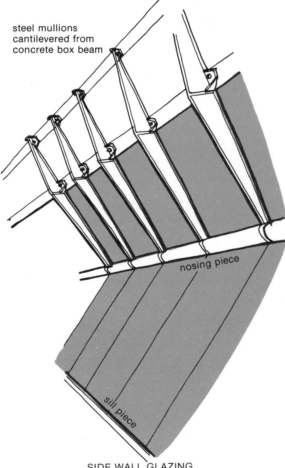

steel mullions cantilevered from concrete box beam

nosing piece

sill piece

SIDE WALL GLAZING

Lifting up the Glass Sheets and Placing Them in Position

First a scaffold platform was built at each level to be glazed. The deck of the platform had to be smooth and level as a floor because the mobile crane would be moving over it.

The cut sheets, packed in felt trays, were lifted up to the platforms by the main tower cranes.

Waiting on the platform was an ingenious mobile crane built by Quick-Steel. It had six vacuum pads on a frame and it picked up each piece of glass before it trundled across the platform into position. By moving its boom each sheet was able to be lifted into the waiting glazing frame, where the final adjustments took place.

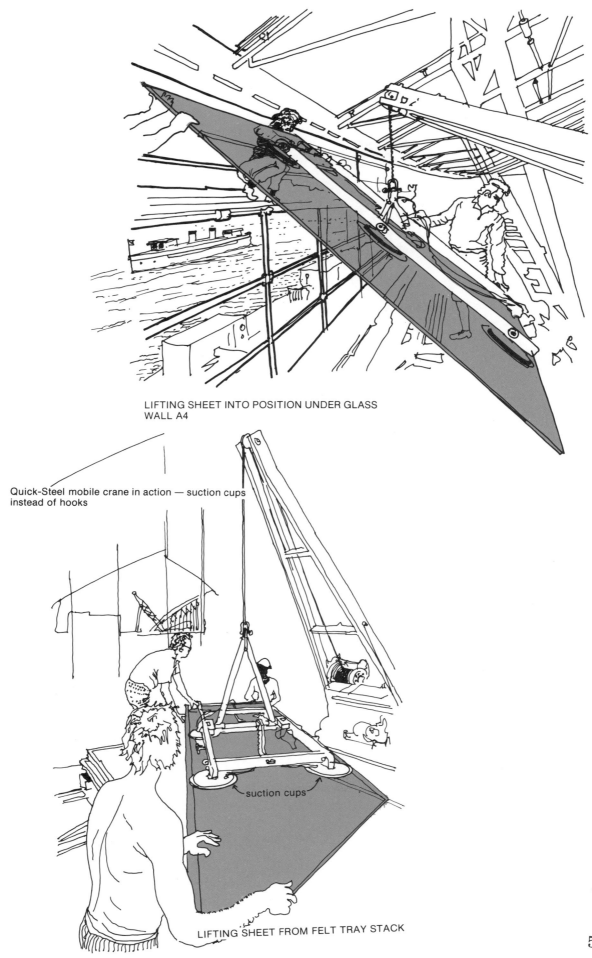

LIFTING SHEET INTO POSITION UNDER GLASS
WALL A4

Quick-Steel mobile crane in action — suction cups
instead of hooks

suction cups

LIFTING SHEET FROM FELT TRAY STACK

57

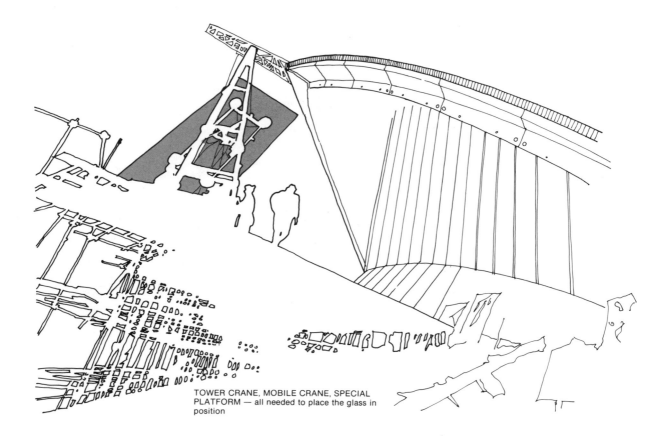

TOWER CRANE, MOBILE CRANE, SPECIAL PLATFORM — all needed to place the glass in position

The Final Adjustment of the Glass

Each sheet of glass was supported on two small stainless steel pins inserted in holes in the glazing bars however, the holes for the pins could not be predrilled in case they were not in the exact spot. Hawker de Havilland devised a special jack and drill rig which clamped on to the glazing bar: the glass sheet, dangling from the mobile crane, was lowered on to the jib. The glass was adjusted for position, then the bar was drilled, the pins inserted and the glass finally lowered into place.

Sealing and Waterproofing

Translucent silicone rubber, which sticks well to glass and resists ultraviolet radiation, was selected for the job. Where it joined glass, the glass edges had been cleaned carefully, just before the sealant was applied. It was squeezed neatly into the cleaned joints with a sealant gun. Where it joined the glazing bars, the metal was first cleaned with solvents, then primed ready to receive the silicone. The glazing bar cover strip was then fixed down tightly over the top to make a mechanical seal.

A GLASS SHEET MOVING INTO POSITION
READY FOR THE FINAL ADJUSTMENT

Who Did It

A group of skilled Sydney glaziers was set up to tackle the project of glazing the Opera House. They gave themselves the title VASOB, made up from the first letters of their names.

LIFTING GLASS INTO LOWER CONE POSITION
— glass wall A4

What's Full of Life and Lives In a Shell?

Opera in the Concert Hall

The Opera House has become a very versatile place so far as stage productions are concerned. Whereas in 1966 and 1967 violent arguments were raging as to what was to take place in the major hall, and the symphony concerts were chosen above everything else, now large scale operas are performed in the Concert Hall. Although there is not a normal theatre stage, the sets are built up on the concert platform and the stage levels are created with scaffolding and additional platforms. There is no curtain, so lighting is used to give special effects when scenes change.

OPERA SET ERECTED ON CONCERT HALL STAGE

YOUNG MUSICIANS IN THE CONCERT HALL

CONCERT IN THE NORTHERN FOYER

Mostly Mozart

Concerts and recitals are given in the northern foyer from time to time, the audience sitting on the stairs. Sometimes the free Sunday recitals are given here too.

Floor Levels, Feet and the Tide

The Opera House, built before metrification of dimensions in the building industry, has all its plans, and the floors themselves, numbered according to how many feet they are above, or below, mean sea level. The lowest floors of the podium are below the water line and the orchestra pit of the Drama Theatre is Level minus eight feet.

The thousands of doors in the Opera House are also numbered according to their level above the sea.

How They Clean the Glass

Quick-Steel, who made the special glass handling machinery to lift the glass into position, invented a gadget that would climb all over the glass areas so that it could be cleaned.

The gadget is called a buggy. A bronze monorail was mounted along the concrete strip under the shells. Along the monorail runs a small carriage and suspended from the carriage is this buggy.

A man can move across the face of the glass (along the monorail) and up and down (by means of the buggy's own winch). The buggy is fitted with rubber suction pads on the side facing the glass wall—the operator flicks a switch, and like a fly, sucks himself on to the surface for safety.

To reach the awkward bits, that is the extremes of the glass walls, a robot fitted with a rotary brush that both scrubs and rinses, is sent out. This robot, with its arteries of water, compressed air and electricity, is controlled by the person in the buggy.

Sounds Interesting

The Doughnuts

Suspended over the stage in the Concert Hall are circular shapes, nicknamed 'the doughnuts'. They are made of plexiglass and their circular convex form is to reflect sound. They are suspended over the orchestra to bounce sound straight back to the players so that they can hear themselves more easily.

The Acoustic Tests

Dr V.L. Jordan, the acoustic expert, explained how different materials were used to represent the audience as the test models became more precise. The models were built to a scale of 1:10. This scale was specially selected because the mathematics of sound used in the tests would relate easily to the real thing.

These first models had varnished fibre boards, to represent reflective ceilings, and fibreglass blankets to represent people. Later models used small blocks of neoprene for people and strips of fibreboard for seat backs. Later still the seats were made of neoprene strips and the individual people were made with neoprene blocks for bodies and cardboard for heads.

Seating Fabrics

The acoustic experts worked out that the seats in the Opera Theatre would be covered with leather so that empty seats would add to the reverberation time. The seats in the Concert Hall would be covered with wool so that the empty seats would absorb sound, like a person sitting in them.

Noise Testing in a Big Way

Guns were fired inside the Concert Hall and the Opera Theatre during the acoustic tests. Someone on stage fired a shotgun and then a pistol, whilst someone else measured the sound on instruments to find out the reverberation times. Only blank ammunition was used!

Keeping Outside Noise Outside

A helicopter hovered above the Opera House and a nearby ocean liner sounded its loudest sirens—but no noise got through the laminated glass, the concrete roof shells, or the special acoustic sandwiches forming cocoons around the auditoriums of the Concert Hall and the Opera Theatre.

Lightning Conductors

The metal railings that are fitted right down the ridge lines of the shells are not handrails —they are lightning conductors.

How to See More of the Sydney Opera House

There are several ways to get a special insight into what happens in and around the building, all organised by the staff of the Sydney Opera House.

Guided Tours of the Auditoriums and Foyers
Run by the Guided Tours Department seven days a week, these tours take you through the places that you would visit if you came to a performance. A lot of the history and details of the building are explained.

Educational Visits
Are run by the staff of the Bennelong Programme, half day, full day or by arrangement. These visits are extremely flexible in content and depend on the interests of the group concerned. Schools and other groups are introduced to a variety of aspects of life in the Opera House.

The purpose of the visits is to build bridges between people involved in the performing arts and people from outside the Opera House. There are no set topics, but subjects range from 'how the building functions—from catering to fire fighting' to 'how the performing companies operate inside the building; sets, costume and decor, from script through to stage performance rehearsals and an introduction to stage production!'

Package Tours
The package includes a guided tour of the Opera House, dinner with wine at the Bennelong Restaurant, and a ticket for a performance.

The Opera House also offers a Harbourside Sydney in a day tour, which includes a walking tour of the old town, The Rocks, a morning coffee cruise on Sydney Harbour, lunch at the Bennelong Restaurant, and a guided tour of the Opera House.

Backstage Tours
These are run by the Guided Tours Department on Sundays only (12 years and over). The tour takes you backstage on a day when no performances are in progress. You see how the stages work and get a glimpse of what it is like to be on the other side of the curtain.

The Library
An important resource centre on the subject of the Performing Arts. It has extensive archives and there are films on how the Opera House was built, why it was built, and details of special things, such as the making of the Olsen mural.

Acknowledgements and Credits

I wish to thank the following individuals, firms and organisations:

for information and advice about the construction and design of the Opera House:

Ove Arup and Partners; The Hornibrook Group; NSW Department of Public Works; Hall Todd Littlemore; Steensen and Varming and Ian McKenzie; Alan Jensen; David Littlemore; Leon Mousett; Ralph Steadman; Keith Parslow; Hamish McLelland; Paul Bondin; Neal Mortensen, Elias Duek-Cohen.

for information and advice about the running of the Opera House:

Sydney Opera House staff—Lloyd Martin; Beatrice Brickhill-Jones; Ralph Bott; Evelyn Klopfer; Fred Callaway; Peter Knight; Don McMurdo; Don Nisbet.

for photographs and drawings which were an inspiration for many of the sketches in this book:

Harry Sowden, Photographer; Max Dupain, Photographer; Jørn Utzon; Arthur Baldwinson; Ove Arup and Partners; The Hornibrook Group; Hall Todd Littlemore; NSW Department of Public Works; Sydney Opera House.

for the original drawings on page 53:

Ove Arup and Partners

for the cartoon on page 63:

Matthew Martin and *The Sydney Morning Herald*

for help with some of the sketches:

caricatures on pages 21 and 25, Tasman Storey;

spherical geometry on pages 36 and 37, Mallika Weerakoon;

helicopter sketch on page 62, Ian McDougall.

Those Who Designed and Built the Sydney Opera House

The text of this book is not long enough to list all those concerned—from time to time names are mentioned, but there was a cast of thousands—all due for credit. The Opera House was produced by a great team effort. For convenience the work was divided into stages—

Stage One—the Podium

Stage Two—the Roofs

Stage Three—the remainder, including glass walls and fitting out

The principal consultants and contractors were:

Jørn Utzon, Architect, Stages 1 and 2

Hall Todd Littlemore, Architects, Stage 3

Ove Arup and Partners, Structural Engineers, Stages 1, 2 and 3

Steenson Varming, Mechanical Engineers, Stages 1, 2 and 3

Julius Poole and Gibson, Electrical Engineers, Stages 2 and 3

Civil and Civic Pty Ltd, Contractors, Stage 1

The Hornibrook Group, Contractors, Stages 2 and 3

There are comprehensive lists of subcontractors and suppliers for Stages 2 and 3 in The Hornibrook Group book, *Building the Sydney Opera House* and in the Journal of the Royal Society. More details, and other aspects of the design and construction not covered in this book, can be found in these publications:

Journal and Proceedings, Royal Society of NSW, Vol. 6, 1973

The Arup Journal, October 1973, published by Longman Australia Pty Ltd

Sydney Opera House Glass Walls, Harry Sowden, published by Harry Sowden

The Sydney Opera House, Vincent Smith, published by Paul Hamlyn Pty Ltd

Building the Sydney Opera House, The Hornibrook Group, published by The Hornibrook Group.